# HOW TO STUDY BIRDS

# HOW TO STUDY BIRDS

*by*

STUART SMITH

B.Sc., Ph.D.

*Photographs by the* Author,

Eric Hosking, F.R.P.S. *and* A. G. Britten.

*Diagrams and Sketches by*

Edward Bradbury, B.Sc.

COLLINS

14 ST. JAMES'S PLACE LONDON

FIRST IMPRESSION DECEMBER, 1945
SECOND IMPRESSION FEBRUARY, 1946
THIRD IMPRESSION MARCH, 1947



*To the memory of*

RICHARD KEARTON


PRINTED IN GREAT BRITAIN
COLLINS CLEAR-TYPE PRESS : LONDON AND GLASGOW

# CONTENTS

# LIST OF ILLUSTRATIONS

# PREFACE

It has been said, probably with truth, that the percentage of people in this country who are interested in birds is greater than in any other country in the world. The number of such people is growing, and will I feel sure, be augmented by many Service men and women who, after being in the main town dwellers, have by reason of their service in the Forces lived for many months and years in wild and lonely places.

Not only does interest in birds cover all classes of society and shades of opinion, but different people watch birds in different ways, and to different degrees of intensity. Thus bird-watchers may range from the person who can name but half a dozen of the common species of birds, and yet can appreciate their high aesthetic appeal, to the trained biologist, whose critical interest is that of the research worker seeking to gain, from the way birds live, some idea of their place in the natural order. Between these two extremes there has been fixed in the past a wide gulf, and a measure of contempt often exists in the scientist for the so-called " bird-lover " who has the anthropomorphic outlook, whilst the bird-lover in his turn regards the scientist as a dust-dry man whose very training and attitude prevent him from appreciating any of the aesthetic appeal that birds may have. Actually, there can be few field-ornithologists, however rigid their scientific attitude, who have not at sometime or other fallen completely under the spell of birds as gloriously free creatures, beautiful of form and often of voice, and this spell can be intensified rather than weakened by a correct and scientific attitude to bird behaviour. By studying the habits of birds and interpreting their actions dispassionately on broad scientific principles, we can arrive at a better understanding of their minds and emotions, and their place in the green world in which they live. Then, truly to know them is to love them.

One phase of bird-watching which has tended to limit its usefulness and interest in the past, has been the cult of the rare bird. This cult has been all-too popular, so that often the main aim of the average bird-watcher has been the recording of rarities in the field which, while it has its limited uses from a distributional point of view, usually means that a day without a rare bird is regarded as disappointing. Certainly, the first view of a rare bird must always be a thrill, but there is much more to bird-watching than that. We need to introduce into our hobby a new aim ; the aim which sets out not to compile long lists of birds seen, but rather to record their actions, postures, and habits. In other words, not only to know which birds live in a given area, but rather *how* they live. It is hoped that this book, which is an attempt to explain in popular language the scientific approach to field ornithology, will at least point the way to new aims and new interests.

In writing this book I have naturally consulted the published work of a great many authorities. I have not thought it wise to interrupt the text by frequent references to the literature, but a complete bibliography and list of references, with an indication of the corresponding page in the text to which they refer, is given at the end. I am especially indebted to Mr. B. W. Tucker, Editor of *British Birds*, and its publishers, Messrs. H. F. & G. Witherby, for permission to use or adapt matter which has appeared in their journal. In addition, Messrs. David Lack, Noble Rollin, H. N. Southern and Colonel Ryves have allowed me to use matter and adapt diagrams from original data published under names. Mr. W. B. Alexander, director of the Edward Grey Institute for Field Ornithology at Oxford, has helped me considerably by searching the literature for special information.

Edward Bradbury has read the manuscript and suggested some valuable emendations. He is also responsible for all the diagrams and sketches. I am greatly in his debt. Richard Fitter has also suggested several improvements to the text, whilst the days I have spent in the field with Eric Hosking have contributed much to my knowledge of birds.

STUART SMITH.

9 Cromwell Avenue,
Gatley,
Cheshire.

*Spring*, 1945.

# Part One

## *A Bird's Year*

## CHAPTER 1

### SPRING JOURNEY

Watching birds, and studying and interpreting their lively ways is, or should be, a round the year hobby, for there is no time when there is not something of interest to see in the world of birds. But there is no doubt that when the year is at the spring, then is the time when most is to be seen, for then events crowd fast, one upon the other, with much coming and going, pairing, nesting, and rearing of families, and all the emotional intensity and physical outlay of the breeding phase of birds. We may therefore with reason decide to start our study of a bird's year at the advent of spring, and to this end let us begin our observations on birds with the return of the summer migrants, and see what we can gain from days spent in the fields, or by the sea-shore armed with nothing but binoculars, note-book and most important of all, an inquiring mind.

In the spring, about the middle of April, we go out of doors and find that the woods and fields are becoming populated, in ever increasing numbers, by birds which were not present during the winter. Most probably it is their songs which first attract our attention ; willow-warblers, chiff-chaffs, cuckoos, and many more are all back and proclaiming to everyone that there they are. They have come northwards for over 2000 miles to breed in the same area in which they were born in some previous spring. How this migratory urge came into being has long been a source of speculation among ornithologists, from the curious theory of a bishop Godwin of Hereford, who held that birds migrated to the moon, and that a man might be carried there by harnessing a number of large birds, to the modern theories based on carefully controlled experiments in aviary-laboratories. A favourite theory with the later nineteenth century ornithologists was that known as the "glacial epoch" theory. According to the more extreme interpretations of this theory, migration arose from the successive advance and retreat of the northern ice-cap, the birds retreating before the ice as it pushed southwards, and returning north again as the ice retracted. In this way, over a succession of ice-ages, birds were said to have evolved a north-south swing which became an inherited faculty. There are many factors which are opposed to this view, not the least of which is the length of time during which the ice-cap covered northern Europe before retreating again. This was a matter of some millions of years, and the retention of an urge in the birds to return to their original home during so long a period of time is unlikely. It is probable that more can be gained by studying present-day conditions than by invoking prehistoric ones, in attempting to explain the origin of migration. The matter is one of immense complexity and so far as we know, no single factor is likely to offer a discrete or clear-cut explanation. In asking why certain birds migrate, the answer that they do so because, under conditions prevailing in the cold season, the normal food supply is not available, appears on the surface to be adequate. But investigation shows that many species are what we know as "partial migrants"; that is, while certain members of the species stay in the breeding area all the year round, others perform long and arduous migrations of a thousand miles or more. It has even been shown that, in certain partial migrants, some of the birds from a single brood may migrate in the autumn, whilst others from the same brood remain at home. The British song-thrush, pied wagtail, and robin are examples of "partial-migrants," and here the food problem cannot explain their migration. Complexities and anomalies thus face the would-be student of migration at every turn. The first thing he must decide on, is a sound definition of migration. Perhaps the best is one which states that "*migration is a movement of population in which there is a definite shift in the centre of gravity of the population.*" In other words the whole or part of a breeding population of high density must transfer itself *en bloc* to an entirely different part of the globe. This movement is totally different from a " dispersal " of birds after the breeding season, where a high density of population is merely dissipated throughout the surrounding area, and does not transfer itself as a population. Examples are afforded by the herring-gull and the lesser black-backed gull. These two birds breed in Britain under similar conditions and in more or less coincident areas, yet in the autumn, the herring-gull scatters around our coasts and may be found there during the winter and rarely goes more than 200 miles beyond its breeding area. The British lesser black-backed gull, on the other hand, truly migrates, reaching the northern tropics and is a comparative rarity in this country in winter. Thus in true migration we get a real abandonment of a summer area in favour of a winter habitation. In addition, this movement must be regular; the sudden " irruptions " of birds like crossbills, waxwings or nutcrackers from the northern pine forests when the cone and berry harvests fail there, cannot be classed as true migration.

While we can only speculate about the reasons which initially lay at the root causes of the evolved habit of migration, we are on much sounder ground when we come to consider the conditions which, at the present moment, will cause a bird to migrate. These conditions are capable of experimental investigation, and some interesting and useful work has been carried out on this problem mainly in Canada and the United States. It has long been suggested that one of the main factors inducing the onset of the migratory urge may be sexual stimulation, brought about by the increasing amount of light to which birds are exposed as the days gradually get longer when the sun swings north again after the winter solstice. One experimenter sought to test this theory in an experimental aviary. He trapped a number of migratory birds (Canadian juncos) in the autumn as they were on their way south to winter quarters and placed them in an aviary lit by artificial means. When caught, the sex-organs of the birds were small and immature. He was able to show that, by manipulating the conditions of lighting, and exposing the birds to gradually increasing amounts of light, they could be brought into breeding condition at any season of the year, *regardless of the temperature.* In addition, an increase in sexual maturity as shown by increased size and pigmentation of the sex organs, could be induced by substituting periods of activity without light, for periods of artificial illumination. Thus a travelling band kept the birds moving about the cages for long periods of time as compared with " control " birds which rested in the normal manner. When killed, the birds subjected to continuous movement had the more developed gonads, or sex-organs. Interesting confirmation of this effect of physical activity on the sexual maturity of birds was obtained by a study of the starlings which roost in inner London. As is well known, thousands of starlings from the area surrounding London use the ledges of the larger buildings such as the National Gallery, several city churches and so on, for communal roosts to which they flock during the winter. Perched on the ledges, they are subject to continuous disturbance from the traffic beneath, whilst the amount of light reaching them high upon the buildings is negligible. It was found that the sex-organs of such London-roosting birds were in a more advanced state of maturity than those of equivalent birds which remained in country districts to roost and were undisturbed during the night. Other experiments have more or less confirmed these findings, and there seems little doubt that it is possible to increase the degree of sexual maturity of birds by the effect of light and of physical activity. It seems doubtful if activity alone, without any light, can initiate the enlargement of the sex organs, though it may add to any enlargement already started by light. When we come to apply these results to the immediate cause of migration, however, the situation is far from clear. It was thought at first that the urge to migrate was associated with the onset of gonad or sex-organ development, and that once the organs had reached full maturity, the urge would subside. The results obtained from releasing birds whose gonads had been artificially brought to *full* maturity, however, did not confirm this view. Thus Canadian juncos which were caught in the United States on their way north during the spring migration, were kept in cages until the time for the spring migration was over, and the birds would normally have been nesting in their northern haunts had they been allowed to proceed. The gonads were developed by this time to a maximum. On being released, however, these birds did not remain in the district, but immediately resumed their migratory journey northwards. Therefore the idea that the migratory urge is associated merely with a state of change in the sex organs is not entirely satisfactory. Psychological, as well as physiological factors enter into the problem. Thus in the group of birds known as the waders (knot, turnstone, sanderling and the like), a large number of immature birds which have wintered in the tropics or even in South Africa, come north with the main tide of spring migrants. Some may be seen about our coasts all summer, yet they do not go on to breed in the Arctic tundra. Such birds, although examination of their sex-organs shows them to be in an immature state, have been induced by some factor, as yet unappreciated, to embark on a long migration. In addition it has been shown that castrated birds will migrate ! A great deal of accurate experimental work will, no doubt, be done in years to come on this problem and we may one day come to the full answer. At the moment, the cause or causes which induce the migratory urge are still undiscovered, and we can at best postulate some inherent rhythm, which induces the restlessness so apparent in birds at the migratory season. This restlessness gradually increases, until a combination of internal and external factors suddenly reaches a critical pitch, the " spring " is released, and the birds are off.

Let us consider the case of a bird which normally spends the winter in north-west Africa, on either side of the tropic of Cancer. It arrived there probably in November from this country, and there it will stay until the migratory urge sets it flying north again. When will it leave the scrub and palms of Africa for England, and how long will it take to do the journey ? As far as the exact time of departure from its winter haunts in Africa is concerned, we may have little accurate knowledge, for the recording of the arrival and departure of birds is not much done in those parts. But the date the birds reach Europe, and the time they will take to progress towards and reach, their breeding areas, may be known with a fair degree of accuracy, since there are many people scattered over Europe who record the arrival and departure of the birds. From them we may be able to obtain sufficient data to enable us to make a map showing the rate of progress northward of certain species during the spring. This has recently been done for several birds of the summer migrant class, namely the swallow, willow-warbler, redstart, wood-warbler and red-backed shrike, by correlating and collating a vast number of observations of the time of the main arrival in spring of these birds at places all over Europe. Then lines joining points where the average date of arrival is the same (called isochronal lines=lines of "equal time") are traced across a map of Europe and in this way we can get a series of lines showing the rate of spread of a species northwards in the spring. Such a map is that in Fig. 1, where the spread of the willow-warbler over Europe is shown. The heavy black lines, with dates on the right-hand end, show the position of the main tide of the birds at fortnightly intervals. The birds reach Gibraltar about the 5th of March, and they reach the northern tip of Norway by June 1st. They have therefore covered approximately 2500 miles in 88 days, or a daily rate of movement northwards of 29 miles a day. It will be noticed that, latitude for latitude, the arrival of the birds is earlier where the spring comes sooner, as on the western sea-board of Europe, but that the rate of spread is quicker where the actual rate of advance of the season is most rapid, as in eastern continental Europe. This is merely a reflexion of the fact that spring "comes with a bound" in those countries with a continental climate. We have to decide on a criterion to tell us when the spring has reached a given place, and we do this by considering the date at which the average temperature, over a number of years, reaches a given value. Lines joining places on the map whose mean temperature (corrected for elevation above sea-level), are identical, are known as isotherms (equal temperature). If we draw in on the map the isotherm representing 48° Fahrenheit, as has been done with the map of Fig. 1, by using dotted lines and labelling the dates on their left-hand ends, we see that the general shape of the isotherms agrees very well with the

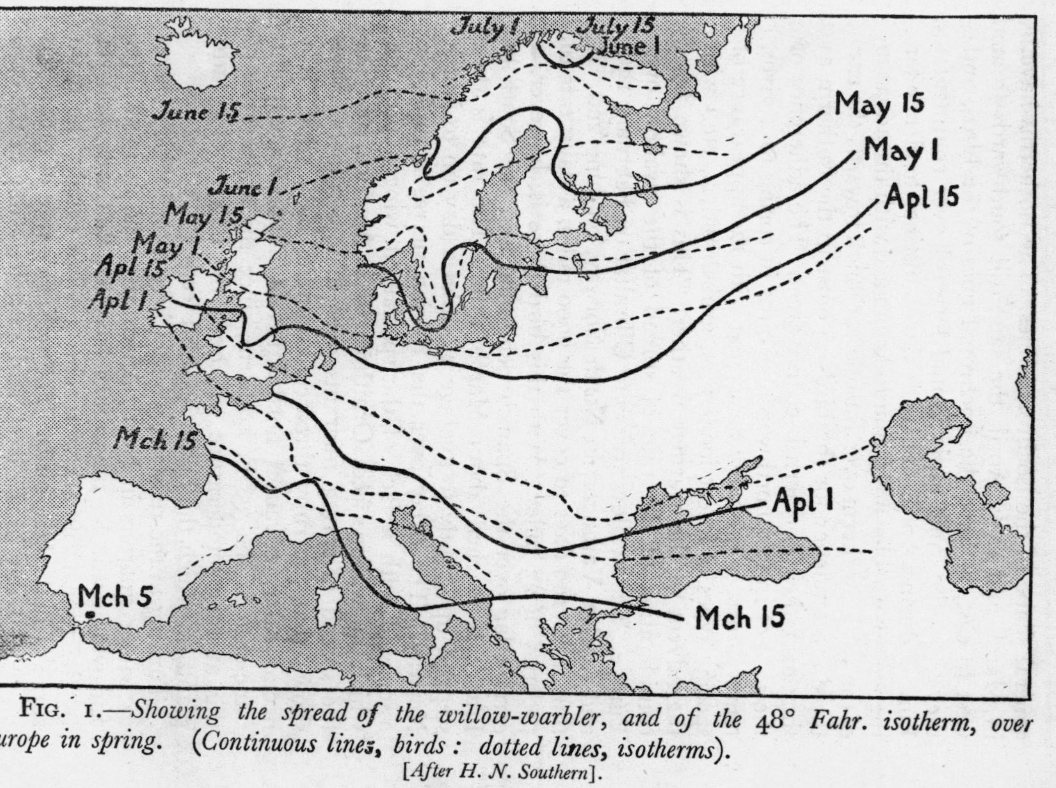


FIG. 1.—*Showing the spread of the willow-warbler, and of the* 48° *Fahr. isotherm, over Europe in spring. (Continuous lines, birds: dotted lines, isotherms).*

[*After H. N. Southern*].

general shape of the isochronal lines. The isotherms have, in March and early April, the same tilt southwards from west to east, as have the isochronal lines of the birds, and they show the same rapid bound forward over continental Europe during April. There is thus a distinct tendency for the willow-warbler migration to keep pace with the advance of the 48° F. isotherm over Europe, although towards the end there is a tendency for the birds to outstrip the isotherm as they near their northern breeding areas. The adherence of the rate of spread northwards of birds in spring to a given temperature, is probably associated with the appearance of specific types of insect food (flies, grubs, spiders, etc.) with the advent of the warmer weather. This is shown by a consideration of the rate of spread of the swallow over Europe. The swallow arrives at Gibraltar on February 13th and reaches Varanger, in North Norway, on June 2nd. It thus takes 109 days to cover the 2000 miles, a daily rate of progress of 23 miles. With this bird there is, however, a certain lag over the Spanish peninsula, and the South of France is reached about March 15th. The rate is then stepped up slightly to average 25 miles a day up to North Norway. The delay over the Iberian sierras is probably associated with a lack of the specialised winged prey on which the swallows feed. Ornithologists in America, studying the spread of spring migrants over their continent, have shown that the ruby throated humming bird, which is a nectar eater, advances northwards at almost exactly the same rate as the 35° F. isotherm, since the appearance of this average temperature will open the flowers of certain plants on which the humming bird feeds.

Turning to the redstart, we find here a bird which leaves its winter quarters in North Africa after the main swallow and willow-warbler migrations have left that area, and yet by the time Denmark is reached, it has caught the main surge of both these birds. The redstart's rate of progress is 33 miles a day in the west, and 41 miles a day in the east. This bird also greatly outstrips the spring (as given by the 48° F. isotherm) from April 15th onwards. Once again, the movement northwards of these birds is probably correlated with food supply. Wood-warblers migrate in the spring at a rate of 22 miles a day in the west and 44 miles a day in the east, whilst the red-backed shrike, which seems to have a main migration trend from Asia Minor across the Balkans to England, progresses at a rate of 55 miles a day. Both the wood-warbler and the red-backed shrike are later migrants than the swallow and willow-warbler, and there is a tendency for the later migrants to have a more southerly limit to their northern breeding range, or in other words, the tide of their migration stops at lower latitudes than does that of the earlier migrants. This may well be due to the fact that the total amount of daylight is already adequate at lower latitudes later in the spring, whereas, earlier in the spring, the early migrants must go farther north to find the equivalent length of day. Since the northern tip of Norway is almost exactly at 70° latitude we can see that this latitude represents the highest at which European passerine birds normally breed. When the redstart reaches there on May 15th, it will encounter about 19 hours of daylight, whilst the wood-warbler, following the redstart about a fortnight later, will then encounter 19 hours of daylight farther south, at about the 60° latitude mark. The wood-warbler range therefore tends to be no farther north than the 60° latitude.

We see then that, in all probability, a bird which left its winter home in Africa will arrive in the Mediterranean area sometime in the first fortnight of March, and that it will spread thence over Europe at a rate which may vary from about 20 to 60 miles a day, depending on a number of factors, not the least of which is the presence of a suitable food supply. There is thus no sudden rush from winter quarters to breeding area in one tremendous and breath-taking jump. Gone are the days of the romantic bird-watcher who believed that the swallow which he saw to-day was but yesterday hawking for flies over the Congo, having flown here with an average speed of 100 miles an hour. Migration we now know to be—as far as that over land is concerned—a slow but steady drift reckoned in miles per day, rather than miles per hour.

When a migrant bird has reached the southern shores of England, it is nearly " home." What exactly does " home " mean to the returning migrant after its spring journey?

Does it mean any spot in these islands where there is suitable cover for its nest and a suitable food supply for the rearing of a family, or does it mean, as if often does to us, one particular spot near to where we were born and bred ? Since the advent of the practice of ringing birds with marked bands round their legs, it has been possible to prove conclusively a fact that had long been suspected, namely that birds normally return each year to the identical area in which they were born, and this applies equally to young and old birds alike. The swallow returns to the barn in which it nested last year, or to one close to it ; the willow-warbler sings in the same coppice, or if not he, then one of his brood from last year ; all come as near to " home " as they can. There arises at once the age-old question of how birds, even those that are returning for the first time, find their way unerringly to this one wished-for spot. The sentimentalists would have us believe that the old birds show the young ones the way, as Tennyson's " Many wintered crow, that led the clanging rookery home ! " Nothing could be further from the truth, and we know, again as the result of careful experimentation, that wild birds possess, in a remarkable degree, the ability to orientate themselves towards a particular spot on the earth's surface, especially when that spot contains their nest and eggs or young. Such an ability is called, for want of a better phrase, the " homing instinct." In considering the reasons for this ability in birds to " home " from great distances, people are apt to be influenced too much by the example of the homing pigeon. This domesticated bird is trained by regular and increasing jumps over the route which will finally be taken in the race, and hence the conclusion is often reached that the homing ability is bound up solely with the fine visual memory which birds are known to possess, the birds recognising at once tracts of country over which they have already passed. In support of this thesis, it is pointed out that in fog, pigeons become hopelessly lost, and that if overtaken by dark, they immediately lie up until daybreak, when they resume their journey. Therefore, it is argued that unless the pigeons can see recognisable landmarks, they cannot home. Yet this scarcely does justice even to the domesticated homing pigeon, for the

" jumps " over which they are trained are often much greater than the limits of visibility. For example, pigeons trained to race to this country from Western France are often jumped over 150 miles of unknown country in France as first stage in the journey, yet at an altitude of 3000 feet, even the horizon, which is the limit of visibility, is only about 60 miles distant. In addition, pigeons have been released at sea with no previous training, 125 miles from land, and got back to their lofts. It seems, therefore, that homing pigeons possess a faculty which gives them a sense of direction towards home, and that they make use of visual cues to tell them when they are getting near to it. Turning now to wild birds, we find the same thing holds, except that the faculty of orientation is probably much better developed in wild birds than it is in the domesticated pigeon, whose domesticity and training may have blunted some of the natural instinct, replacing it by speed and endurance of flight, and greater reliance on visual cues. Many experiments have now been carried out, on all manner of wild birds, to test their ability to get back home after removal for varying distances. In America, some noddy terns and sooty terns nesting on islands in the Gulf of Mexico were taken by ship 850 miles over the ocean to an area which these species do not normally inhabit, and there released. Many found their way back. Here there can be no question of landmarks guiding the birds, at least until they are almost home. Other experiments have been conducted in this country on sea-birds, namely on the puffin, storm-petrel and Manx shearwater. Puffins released at Start Point, returned to Skokholm Island, Pembrokeshire, a distance of 125 miles direct or 220 miles by shortest sea route, in 5 days. Storm-petrels, released from the same place, returned in 6 days, whilst other storm-petrels, released on the Isle of May (Firth of Forth), which was 340 miles direct (involving a land crossing of north Britain) or 800 miles by shortest sea route from Skokholm, returned in 11 days. Shearwaters, birds which never normally come to land except to breed, exhibited remarkable ability to " home," even over land areas. One released at Birmingham, 90 miles from the nearest sea and 160 miles from home, got back safely ; another released inland at Frensham, Surrey, got back in 24 hours, a distance of 200 miles direct and 390 miles by the nearest sea route. Finally, some of the Skokholm shearwaters were taken by air to Venice. The interesting point about this experiment is that the Mediterranean is outside the normal range of the Manx shearwater. The distance was 930 miles direct, and 3700 miles by nearest sea route. Yet one of the birds got back in 14 days.

As far as many land birds are concerned, we have similar striking evidence of this homing instinct. Swallows which were nesting at Bremen, Germany, were taken by air to Croydon, a distance of 428 miles, and there released. The first birds were back within 4 days. The same investigator was able to show that swallows would return to Berlin from London, Munich, Venice and Athens. Red-backed shrikes got home to the Berlin area from Marseilles ; wrynecks from Munich, Venice and Salonica. There is a certain amount of evidence, however, that the homing instinct is not equally powerful in all species of wild bird, and it appears that some sedentary types may not possess it in any marked degree. Thus the goshawk, a resident species which does not normally stray far from its native forests, appears to have little or no ability to find its way back from long distances. The American counterpart of our sparrow-hawk, known as the sharp-shinned hawk, did not return home even from a distance of a few miles.

Certain birds exhibit a queer reaction in not returning to their home immediately on being released, but of returning there in later years. Thus some experiments in America in which golden-crowned sparrows were removed for a considerable distance from their breeding area resulted in some of the birds returning at once, whilst others did not put in an appearance until the following season. Others again, and this is more curious still, returned next season, not to the home area, but to the area in which they were released ! This latter habit was surprisingly exhibited by some white storks which were taken from Poland to Finland, 830 miles due north of their nesting area. Finland is normally well outside the range of the white stork and hence such a large and rare bird was readily noticed by many people, and it was possible to keep track of the movements of these birds with considerable accuracy. After release at Harviala in Finland, the birds correctly headed south until they arrived at the Gulf of Finland. They then seemed completely baffled by the wide stretch of sea, and promptly returned to the place where they were released. This showed the same queer attachment to an entirely new locality. Many experiments have been carried out on storks, which are particularly suitable birds for this type of investigation, being large migrant birds, easily identified, and associating with man in their nesting areas. Polish scientists have shown that storks nesting near Lwow, in central Poland, could get back from Warsaw 187 miles north-west, Bukharest 415 miles south, and Palestine 1420 miles south. All the birds had young in the nest and were ringed, and colour-marked by dyed feathers, for identification. A recovery of 75 per cent was obtained of the total of released birds. The rate of return varied from 103 miles a day for the Bukharest birds, to 116 miles a day for the Palestine birds. The behaviour of the birds on release was identical in all cases ; they took time to clean and preen their feathers, then took wing, circled, and headed straight for home. The sense of direction seemed unerring, but we cannot yet tell through what part of a bird's physiological or psychological make-up this sense is operated. There have been many suggestions to explain it, the most persistent one being the " terrestrial magnetism " theory. This theory suggests that birds are able to sense, in some way, the direction of the lines of force of the earth's magnetic field, some people even suggesting that each part of the earth's surface, having as it has a characteristic of terrestrial magnetism known as the " dip " at that place, can be pin-pointed by a magnetic recording mechanism somewhere in the bird's body. The theory was supported by nebulous reports of homing pigeons which, released near large broadcasting stations, were said to be unable to orientate themselves in the neighbourhood of the aerials. Once again, the theories have failed to stand the hard facts of controlled experiments. Thus, the same Polish scientists tested the homing abilities of storks which had magnetised iron bars fixed to their heads, of such a strength that they would completely over-ride any effect of the earth's magnetic field. There was no difference in the ability of these storks to find their way home compared with " control " birds with iron bars of the same size, but not magnetized, affixed in the same position. So the homing ability remains a mystery. If we could explain it we should be getting near to the solution of the mystery of migration itself, for in spite of all the work so far carried out, we still have to confess that we are " worlds away " from understanding this most mysterious and most exciting of bird problems. All we *can* say is that birds seem to possess a sense of geographical position which enables them to orientate themselves towards a desired spot, and that they probably fly blind along this route until they pick up landmarks and visual cues which tell them where they are. There remain one or two points to discuss before we can finally see our bird settled in the favoured family spot somewhere in England. In the first place, the observant bird-watcher who chronicles the time of arrival of the migrant species each spring will quickly notice that it is the male birds that arrive first. We shall see later that from the point of view of the establishment of a " territory " in which to breed, such an arrangement has definite survival value. As far as migrant birds are concerned we do not know definitely whether the cock birds keep separate from the hens and young of the year, in their winter quarters. Most of the migrant birds which visit this country in winter from Scandinavia are of species in which the cock and hen birds are not much different in plumage, such as redwing, fieldfare, starling and so on, so we cannot draw many conclusions from the flocks we see about the fields in winter. They may be all cocks, all hens, or a mixture of both. But we know that in the case of the chaffinch, the flocks are often composed mainly of cock or hen birds, and the question of the composition of winter flocks both here and in other " reception " areas for summer migrants is one which needs investigation. In its winter quarters therefore our bird may have been in a flock composed of males of the same species. When they left their quarters to come north on the spring journey, how did the birds come ? Did they come along a well-defined route all together in a flock, all stopping at the same feeding places, and roosting together in the same wood or hedgerow? Or did they set out as individuals on a drift northwards, fanning out and pursuing a lone, variable, but certain course towards home? As far as the route taken is concerned, we come immediately on a certain divergence of opinion, for some contend that birds migrate along well-defined routes, the following of which is often said to be a faculty inherited through generations of birds, and it is even stated at times that the routes may follow old valleys and geological features now completely obliterated by the sea. At the other end of the scale we have the "broad-front" theory, which holds that birds in general migrate over a wide area, a great wave, many miles across, passing over and through the countryside. As so often happens, the truth probably lies somewhere between the two theories, but there seems little doubt that, if the conditions of the country warrant it, broad-front migration is the general rule. The exponents of the fixed route theory point to the Nile Valley as a great migration route from eastern Europe to Africa, whilst in this country the regular appearance of migrant birds at fixed places like reservoirs and sewage farms has been used as an argument in favour of definite routes. Thus waders like the curlew-sandpiper will be seen first on the east coast; a few days later some may be seen on the reservoirs on the Pennine moors; then on the Cheshire meres, and so on. Superficially this looks like a definite route across England from east to west, but it can just as easily be explained if we suppose that this wader is migrating on a broad front principle, and that it merely alights at suitable feeding places situated along the wave-front of its advance. Those birds on the wave-front which do not find such suitable spots, merely pass straight on until they do, and these birds we never see along our so-called route. Thus the impression of a definite flight-line may be entirely false. There is, however, considerable evidence that geographical features may compress the broad front inwards in places until it narrows to such an extent that the steadily moving wave becomes a torrent of birds, like water pouring through a sluice. The geographical features which accomplish this may be wide areas of sea, or high mountain barriers, so that we get places like Gibraltar where hordes of birds pass through on migration. Italy too acts as a sort of conduit for birds from central Europe. But there is evidence that the birds fan out again as soon as these constricting features are passed, and broad front migration over North Africa, and even, contrary to many opinions, over the Sahara itself, is now a well-established fact. The fighting in the North African desert during the war gave many soldier-ornithologists the chance to study migration in the desert, and some surprising observations were made. One observer was on the famous cross-desert expedition which set out across the Sahara from Kufra to attack the oasis of Jalo, 400 miles westwards. He noticed that the lorries forming the convoy were used by many warblers and other small migrants for shelter at night. Wherever they were in the desert (and that is the point to be noted), as soon as the convoy stopped for the night, warblers, chats, whitethroats and other small birds appeared out of the sky and rushed to shelter beneath the lorries and tents of the convoy. One officer had to abandon his car " 150 miles from anywhere " in the desert, and when he retrieved it later found 20 small birds sitting beneath it ! Oases, too, throng with birds but this is also a reflexion of the fact that those passing the immediate neighbourhood descend there as they do at the English reservoirs, meres and sewage farms.

So we see that broad-front migration tends to be the general rule, and it is probable that the birds drift northwards for the main part of the journey more or less as individual figures. Naturally as they near their breeding haunts, the possibility of linking with more of their fellows increases, but as far as the spring migration is concerned we rarely see, in the passerine birds, the large migratory flocks which often characterise the autumn flight, and it is usual for the birds to drift in in ones and twos.

## CHAPTER 2

### ENSURING A PLACE IN THE SUN

THE COCK BIRDS have now, we will suppose, arrived back at, or near to, the spot where they nested last year, and any one of them may find himself in the self-same spinney, or hedge-row, or reed-bed. What are his immediate reactions? At first, for a day or so, and especially if the weather is cold and windy, he has no very vigorous reactions to his environment. He may sing a little, and even consort at times with other cock birds of his kind, wandering around with them in the area. But we notice that certain steadily increasing tendencies are present in our bird, and these tendencies are greatly accentuated by the coming of warm spring-like conditions. We see that he exhibits an increasing tendency to stay in one particular area; some small corner of a meadow, or a clump of trees, and that from some vantage point within this area, he sings with increasing vigour and for increasingly long periods. Soon the favoured area is rarely abandoned, and, what is more, any birds of his own species are resolutely attacked and chased away. Sometimes he will attack a bird other than one of his own species, but it is usually a case of mistaken identity, the bird often being one of similar shape and size to himself. Our cock bird thus becomes thoroughly aggressive. He shouts defiance from his vantage point, singing loud and long; he rushes madly at birds of his own species and attempts to drive them away, using stances and attitudes in which any coloured or striking parts of his plumage may be fluffed up or erected to enhance the terror-effect. He gapes his mouth wide at his opponent and often pants visibly. Sometimes he may hiss like a snake. Usually the intruder bird rapidly removes itself from our bird's area and he returns to his vantage point to sing and watch. Our bird is pegging-out his claim to a certain area of land in which, when his hen bird arrives, the pair will most probably build their nest and rear their young. It is from such actions on the part of the cock birds in the early spring that the theory of territory in the bird world has been formulated. Suspected for many years from superficial observation, it received considerable support from a series of sustained and careful observations by one famous ornithologist, although its comprehensiveness has since been queried especially in regard to the significance of a territory as a guaranteed source of food supplies. A great deal depends on the definition of " territory," but the simplest one is, perhaps, that which defines it as " any defended area." What are the biological advantages of the struggle for a territory? The most obvious one is that it ensures a fairly even distribution of any one species over areas suitable to that species. It is in a way, a struggle for elbow-room. Added advantages of this acquisition of a territory can readily be deduced. For instance, it may often mean that, given normal conditions, an exclusive area is available, close to the nest, from which food for the young can easily be obtained. From the ease with which young birds in the matter of an hour or so succumb to cold and lack of food, it is obviously of importance to have an ample food supply closely and readily available. But a word of caution is necessary about the size of such a territory which is absolutely essential for any particular species. It would be most unwise to assume that the boundaries of the territory of any particular bird which we may be studying necessarily enclose the minimum area required by that species for the successful rearing of a brood. On the contrary, our bird-watching soon tells us that they rarely do so. For example, we may take the case of a group of yellow wagtails breeding on a small Cheshire farm. The cock birds arrive during the third week in April, and by the first week of May are well established in their territories. These territories are easily mapped by careful observation, and on a small ten-acre strip of the farm, given over to market garden produce and hence in a good state of cultivation, we can find three cock yellow wagtails singing from prominent clods of earth or in one case, the upraised shafts of a farm roller. But the three territories are by no means equal, that is to say each is not exactly one-third of ten acres. We find that one cock, the

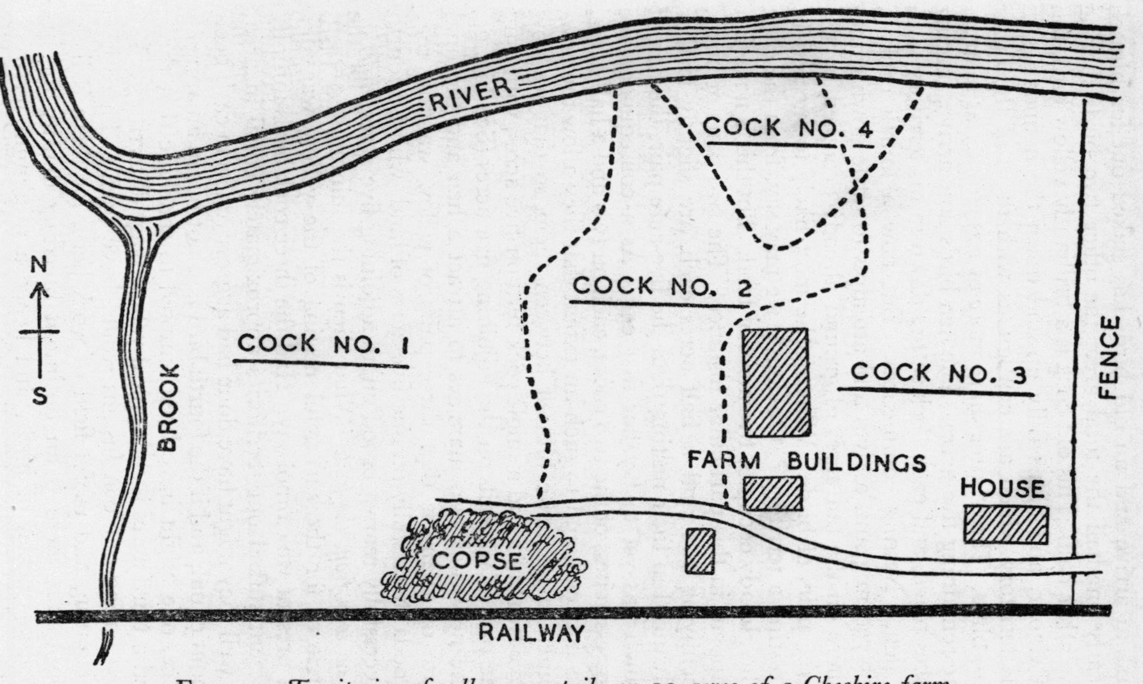


FIG. 2.—*Territories of yellow wagtails on 10 acres of a Cheshire farm.*

first to arrive and an old bird, has staked out for himself nearly one-half the total area, the other two birds sharing the other half. This old cock is a brilliantly yellow bird, full of vigour, and flies wildly up and down the boundaries of his territory which are contiguous with those of the other two birds. These latter share more or less equally as to area, the remaining five acres. The hen birds now arrive, pairing takes place, and each cock settles down in his territory with a hen. Nesting commences. But now a fourth cock, a delayed migrant, arrives and attempts to settle down somewhere on the ten acres of ground already occupied by the three pairs of birds. Where is he most likely to succeed in wresting a territory? Obviously we may say, from the cock who already occupies five acres of land. But this is not what happens in this particular instance. The two pairs of birds, occupying two and a half acres each, are slightly farther advanced in their nesting than the five-acre pair, the hen of which has yet to lay her first egg. As a consequence the aggressiveness of the two cocks, each on two and a half acres, has declined, and to such an extent that they allow the newcomer to insinuate himself between them, so that we now have two pairs and a single cock bird on five acres, with only one pair of wagtails on the adjoining five acres (See Fig. 2). The new cock also manages to attract a hen and the final state of affairs is that three pairs of yellow wagtails rear broods successfully on one five acres of land, whilst a fourth successfully rears a brood on an adjoining five acres, *differing in no way from the first.* What then is the minimum area of territory for the successful nesting of the yellow wagtail? At present we cannot say. Had the three cock birds initially present staked out territories approximately equal in area, as well they might have done had aggressiveness in each been about equal, and if the fourth bird had not put in an appearance, one might have been tempted to conclude that three and a third acres is the typical yellow wagtail territory. Yet how wrong our conclusions would have been! There is a fascinating and useful field of work here, for there is little doubt that there *is* an optimum breeding density for individual species of birds, and hence a minimum territory below which it would be disastrous to go. What this territory is for each species we do not yet know. It has been suggested, that as a rule, it is of the order of half an acre, but the data available are as yet far too scanty for this to be other than a very rough estimate. It must obviously be correlated with type of country and hence available food supply. In the case of our yellow wagtails, the market garden country in which they nest teems with insect life. Cabbages are fine breeding grounds for caterpillars, and the birds have no difficulty in finding food for the young. Probably this area would support a pair of yellow wagtails on each half-acre of ground. But transfer our wagtail population to an area of rough pasture, or fell-side sheep walks, and the picture is immediately different. The importance of the amount of food available in a given area in relation to territory in the bird world is brought out by a consideration of birds which nest in colonies ; birds like the gulls, terns, cliff-nesting guillemots and razorbills and so on. Here we have an unlimited source of food supply readily available in the sea, and territorial competition in the feeding area is obviously unnecessary and indeed, almost impossible. But in the case of such birds, there is often a great scarcity of available nesting sites. Guillemots nest on narrow shelves on the cliff face, and the birds fight bitterly for favoured ledges. The "territory" then becomes the small area of a few square feet round the nest. The question of colony-nesting birds is, really, a weak link in the chain of reasoning which holds the territory theory together as a comprehensive whole. Rooks and herons usually nest in colonies in closely packed groups of trees, and range the surrounding country for food. The only competition appears to be for nest-sites in the trees, and for sticks and nesting material. Herons show little animosity towards one another at the heronry. Terns prefer to mass together in the breeding season on one favoured shingle strip when miles of similar coast line, on which they could distribute themselves evenly in "territories," remain untenanted. Such colonial nesting is said to have survival value, since the mass of nesting birds protects the eggs and young of unguarded nests from predators when the parents are away at the feeding grounds. Yet other birds, nesting in similar sandy shingle on the shore, like oyster-catchers and ringed plovers, space their nest out in apparent territories and do not need the protection of colonial nesting. There is thus a great deal of watching and recording to be done before we can tell what intimate significance territory has for individual species of birds. Territory as a *general* concept is probably true, but its quantitative basis is far from being completely known. For colony nesting birds, the territory (if such it can be called in this case) seems to be a few square feet round the actual nest-site, and the wider implications of the territory theory, such as its significance for a guaranteed food supply, must be modified. Many interesting cases which represent modifications to the theory are available for study. Thus the male ruffs do not defend a given area of fen-land, but assemble on a flat piece of ground often called the "tourney-ground." Here each male bird stamps out a small piece of ground often only a square yard or so in area, and here displays aggressively to his neighbours by lowering his head, spreading the wonderful "ruff" of feathers around the neck, and generally behaving on his little mound of earth just as a small passerine bird would do over his acre or so. The hen birds, or reeves, come to this stamping ground and pair formation takes place there, probably quite away from any future nest-site. Black grouse behave in a similar way. Their "tourney-grounds" or "leks" are open spaces in the pine and birch forests they inhabit, and here the blackcocks display and fight in little groups, and the greyhens come for pairing and coition. Black-headed gulls and similar colony-nesting gulls have small but ill-defined areas near the nest which may be "defended" against other birds of the colony. Each colony of black-headed gulls appears to consist of a number of unit-groups of nests within the colony, and aggressive reaction by a bird of such a group is greater towards those from other groups than towards birds belonging to its own group. As far as jackdaws are concerned, the whole colony acts as a unit from the territorial point of view, but within the colony, there is a social precedence order, arrived at by aggressive behaviour involving pecking at rivals. The chief bird pecks those who are his nearest rivals in the order, but disdains to do so to the lower-scale birds. As a communal unit, the whole flock will attack anything which threatens its well-being, and this communal instinct is so well marked that the birds will defend black material like a black bathing costume, a black quill feather, or a black farmyard hen, against possible danger !

The various types of aggressive display used by birds in obtaining and defending their " living space " provide a fascinating study. A point which must strike the bird-watcher very forcibly as he watches birds during this period of aggressive display and the succeeding period of nuptial display, is the marked similarity that often exists between the types of action and posture used in defiance and those used in courtship. Very often the two displays appear practically identical, for the same prominent parts of the plumage are used in the same manner. Coloured adornments find great use in threat postures as symbolic of, or preparatory to, combat, and serve to advertise widely, that the displaying bird is established in a territory and prepared to defend it. In this way the defence of the territory is often achieved without combat, which is a desirable state of affairs. But when we see the same actions used by the cock bird towards his hen when courting her prior to mating we must not assume that the emotional reactions causing the two displays are the same, or even similar. This will be apparent to those who are prepared to watch birds intimately and at close range. It is here that concealment in a hide tent placed in their territories is able to give results which reveal small but essential differences in movement and large ones in emotional approach. Emotionally, the key lies in studying the expression in the bird's eye. When attacking a rival, a cock yellow wagtail sometimes fluffs up its yellow breast, throws its head back and pirouettes round dragging wing-tips and tail on the ground. It has a very similar display in courting the female. Yet the two emotional states accompanying these reactions are poles apart; the eye in the former case has a fiery flashing of defiance which is quite unmistakable; in the latter there is certainly emotional excitement, but the eye shows the softer lustre of sexual desire. This point is also beautifully illustrated by the use to which the goldcrest puts its flame-coloured crest in both threat and nuptial display.

In both displays, the crest is erected, expanded and sometimes vibrated, so that a flame of orange-red colour seems to cover the whole of the top of the head. There is little difference in the actual arrangement of the plumage, nor in the stances adopted by the displaying bird during the two types of display, but there is certainly a most subtle difference between the emotional states of the cock in the two cases. Threat postures have at their root the instinct of fear, as may be seen from the threatening attitudes adopted by many young birds, like owlets, when approached at the nest. Courtship display and posturing arise from sexual excitement, and again the expression in the eye of the bird gives us the clue to its intimate emotional state. The Teutonic approach to the study of birds, which seems to demand that a given set of visual stimuli automatically elicit a set response, would no doubt deny the existence of markedly different emotional states accompanying identical reactions. Yet the watcher who sees birds plainly and at close quarters, will soon realise that, while he must guard himself rigidly against any return to the bad old days of Victorian and Edwardian sentimentalism about the " wonders of nature," he must be equally on his guard against regarding the small brain which controls a bird's life as one entirely without any degree of freedom of action. A typical example of the Teutonic approach is the suggestion, which needs confirmation, and is certainly not universal, that certain threat and courtship displays are similar only in those birds in which the plumage of the two sexes is alike. Under emotional stress, the cock bird then reacts, it is said, with a fixed set of posturings and displays in the presence of any bird of his species, whether cock or hen. If the bird opposite to him be a cock, it responds likewise and combat ensures ; if it be a hen she responds with a different set of reactions, by crouching, or by ignoring the cock, and thus sexual recognition is assured, together with differential sexual behaviour. The error in this approach seems to be in the assumption that the emotional state eliciting all display is a common one, and that external circumstances alone cleverly arrange that the subsequent behaviour of the birds shall not result in chaos. It is the approach of the chemist rather than the naturalist : the approach that regards birds as biological elements which, mixed together under a given set of conditions, invariably follow a given set of reactions resulting in a fixed and constant end-product ! Such reasoning, which has evolved out of a natural and initially healthy desire to eliminate anthropomorphism and substitute laws of behaviour which would not demand from the bird too high a standard of intelligence, has now swung the pendulum too far to the other extreme.

Some very interesting and sometimes amusing, experiments can be carried out by studying the aggressive reactions of birds at mirrors placed in their territories, or to stuffed birds, or pieces of coloured cloth or feathers having the same colours as the prominent plumage parts used in display. Thus before a triple-sided looking glass, a cock pied wagtail displayed and postured to its own image, especially displaying its black chin and throat. A blackbird crouched before the mirrors with outstretched neck and raised feathers ; a great tit continually displayed its black throat and breast markings. Robins will attack stuffed robins from which the head has been removed, the red feathers from a robin's breast fixed by themselves on a wire, and even a piece of red rag. Colours thus play an important part in the stimulating of threat display, and it is significant that the replacement of the red breast on a stuffed robin by a dull brown colour elicits no aggressive display from live robins. The robin is an interesting bird because although it has an elaborate threat display, it has no nuptial display to speak of. In addition, its threat display is often accompanied by considerable singing on the part of the displaying birds, and often, when actually fighting, the two combatants will maintain loud and sustained song one against the other. That song is a very powerful weapon of bird aggression is obvious from a study of the methods employed by cock birds to advertise and defend their territories. The prominent vantage-point chosen within the territory from which song is poured forth during the claim-staking period enables the cock bird to advertise his presence and his possession audibly as well as visually. In addition, it is almost certain that the song helps to attract the female bird to the territory and thus ensure that successful pair-formation occurs. But there must be other reasons than these two of defiance and enticement to give a complete explanation of why birds sing. It is probable that the fundamental reason for bird song lies within the bird itself, in the state of its endocrine, or ductless gland system, and that the uses *external* to itself to which the bird puts this song, are merely natural adaptations of the faculty, which help the bird to survive. But this view also allows of the type of bird song where there is no apparent utilitarian motive, and give point to the old idea, at times ridiculed by a few extremists in the biological world, that birds can and do sing merely from a sense of well-being. The behaviour of certain birds in autumn illustrates this point. The robin, as all know, particularly since the details of its life have recently been so thoroughly investigated, recommences singing in early autumn, and also adopts winter territories which are defended as violently as are those associated with the nest. Here autumn and winter song have a survival value. But other birds show an autumnal recurrence of sexual activity and with it song, which does not reveal itself in territorial aggressiveness. Thus the song-thrush begins to sing again in November, but will feed quite placidly with others of its kind on lawns and meadows. Starlings too, that is the resident race in Britain, begin singing again in October and often visit old nesting sites ; yet this bird remains essentially one which feeds in packs in the autumn and winter. Here song has no obvious utilitarian significance, and is best explained in terms of the internal state of the bird. What is this rather mysterious " internal state " to which we have already referred ? It is only within comparatively recent years that anything like a full understanding of the factors governing the internal physical state of our bodies has been gained. We know now, however, that many of the essential physical functions of the bodies of animals are entirely governed by special glands. Glands are normally of two main types, namely those which are connected directly with a particular part of the body which they serve with special secretions ; and those others which, because they have no tube or duct to connect them to a part of the body, are known as *ductless* glands. It is with these latter that we are mainly concerned here, for the ductless glands manufacture some very remarkable chemical substances, which they pass by diffusion into the bloodstream. These substances are called " hormones " or chemical messengers, and their presence in the blood stream governs in a remarkable degree not only the health of the animal, but also many of its external physical characters. One such gland is called the thyroid gland ; when the thyroid gland is not working as it should do, we get the disease known as exophthalmic goitre. Another gland is the pituitary gland, which is slung just below the brain at the back of the head, and a section or " lobe " of this gland is able, by passing hormones of a certain kind into the blood, to stimulate the sex-glands. Then these sex-glands, or gonads as they are called, are induced in their turn to pass special sex-hormones into the blood and these are the governing cause of any sexual manifestations a bird may show. There are two remarkable things about sex-hormones. The first is that they are of two kinds, male and female sex-hormones, which are respectively responsible for the male and female characteristics of the bird. Thus the male birds may normally show their sex by brighter colourings, ability to sing, aggressive behaviour and so on. The female bird, on the other hand may have duller colouring, be able only to chirp or call, and generally have the external characters we associate with hen birds. Now we come to the second remarkable fact. In the bodies of some female birds there are glands which can secrete both kinds of sex-hormone, and the mere fact that a bird has female characters is merely a reflexion of the fact that in its case there is an excess of one particular type of hormone over the other. There is liable at times to be a delicate balance between the two types, and if for some reason, a little more male sex hormone is produced at one particular time of the year, or for some particular cause, then it is possible not only for the male birds to resume sexual activity, but for the female birds to assume some of the male's characteristics. Thus we know that some of the robins which sing in the winter, and map out territories for themselves, are hen birds. With the onset of autumn, they have so far assumed male characteristics as to be able to sing, and to want to defend a territory. In the same way, hen starlings will assume in autumn the yellow bill of the cock bird, and will sing as it does. It has been shown experimentally, in support of such a view, that injection of male sex hormone into a female canary will cause it to sing like a male. In addition, the classical cases of crowing domestic hens, many of which are well authenticated, are all to be traced to some such cause. Thus in the case of one domestic hen which after laying a number of eggs for two years and actually hatching out several broods of her own chicks, suddenly began to grow a cock's comb, wattles and curled tail feathers, and to crow like a cockerel, it was found that an internal growth was pressing on the ovaries of the bird, suppressing its female characteristics, and allowing the male ones to become dominant.

Not all birds use song to advertise their territory, for indeed there are some territorial species without a true song. The woodpeckers are birds with little or no true song, but they substitute for it the well-known " drumming " sound accomplished by a rapid tapping with the bill on a dead branch of a tree. Other " territorial drumming " is that of the common snipe, which advertises its presence over its nesting area by the production of a bleating sound in the air. It is of interest to note that in both of these cases there has been in the past a certain amount of doubt about the actual cause of the two sounds. It has been suggested that both were true vocal notes, but we know now without question that the drumming of the woodpecker is made by a definite tapping of the bill against dead or broken branches, whilst the snipe's drumming is associated primarily with the two outer feathers of the bird's tail. The woodpecker chooses a branch of such dimensions that its own frequency of tapping, usually about 10 taps per second, will set the branch vibrating in sympathy, or by " resonance " as it is called. This is why only certain branches are used for drumming. A light tap then produces a disproportionately loud sound. Vibrating in sympathy, or " resonance," accounts for many similar, but better known examples of a loud noise from a light tap. Thus car-owners will know that at a certain speed, a car may run quite quietly, but that as the speed is increased, a loud rattle may suddenly appear. The vibrations of the engine have reached a critical pitch at which loose doors, nuts or other parts begin to vibrate in sympathy, and a very loud noise may then be produced from a much smaller noise.

The snipe only makes its drumming sound when descending rapidly in flight, in a steep dive, and then the outer tail feathers stand out at right angles to the line of the bird's descent, and it is the tremulous vibrations of these feathers which produce the sound. The half-closed wings also vibrate slightly so that the air-stream is alternately deflected across the leading edges of the two feathers from above to below and back again. In this way, it has been demonstrated recently, a series of damped vibrations of the feathers are set up which prevent the amplitude of the vibrations from becoming so large as to injure the web-structure of the feathers. The bleating note rises and falls with the amplitude of the feather-vibrations.

An interesting exercise for the student is to construct charts showing the times of the year during which the different species of birds may be heard singing, at the same time noting weather conditions, wind, temperature, and so on. There are many ways in which data for such charts may be collected, and for the observer who cannot make continuous observations there are several pitfalls to be avoided. Thus if one can only go out once a day at variable times in relation to sunrise and sunset, the results are obviously not going to have the significance of a similar set of data collected twice a day at fixed times in relation to sunrise and sunset. One observer was able to obtain some useful results which had considerable value by the following method. He decided on two separate routes or walks, each of which took him about 25 minutes to traverse. The routes were over Surrey downland, one through an area with some cultivated land and gardens, the other taking him through a large wood. He divided the months into three equal periods of ten days each, and decided to do 6 counts on one route and 6 on the other for each ten-day period. For each of the two groups of 6 counts, three were done at 8 a.m. in the morning, and three at 6 p.m. in the evening. He thus got a dozen counts for each ten-day period, six on each of the two routes. His

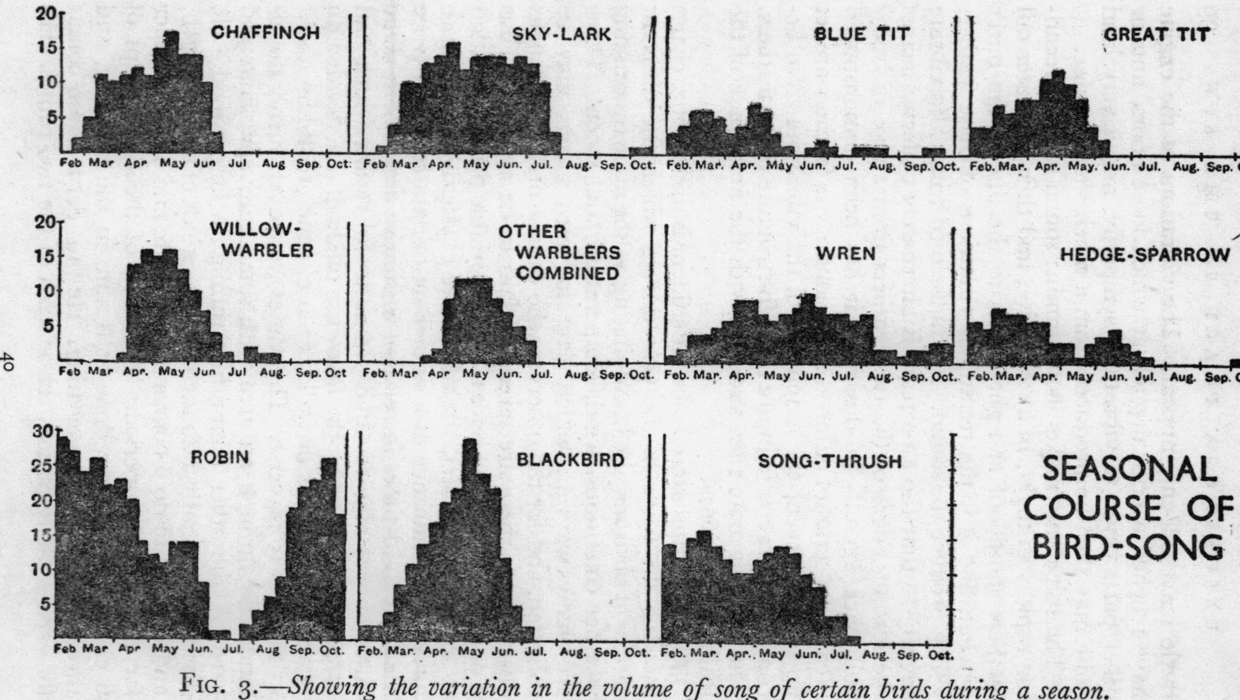


FIG. 3.—*Showing the variation in the volume of song of certain birds during a season.*
[*After Cox*].

method of recording was to count the total numbers of each species heard singing during his walks. The method is attractive because it gives, not only the distribution of song of any one particular species over a period of the year, but also a measure of the amount of that song. It also gives us a comparison of the amount of song in the morning compared with that in the evening. The graphs obtained by this observer are given in Fig. 3 where for the species indicated the total number of birds heard singing during the various ten-day periods are plotted graphically. Considering only the period February to July, the charts fall into two groups. There are those which show a steady mounting of the volume of song up to a peak and then a gradual falling off again. Such song is typified by the blackbird which has a " high peak period " in May, with steep sides to the graph on either side of this peak. The warblers, great tit, skylark and chaffinch are similar, though their peaks are of variable acuteness. The skylark has a " plateau " from April to June when it sings steadily and long. On the other hand, evidences of a *double* hump are given by the song-thrush, blue tit, and hedge-sparrow, which decline somewhat after the " first careless rapture " of early spring, and revive again in June and July. The robin shows especially the remarkable autumn revival of song so characteristic of this bird and to which we have already referred. Results obtained by this method of counting also enable us to determine whether birds sing more in the morning than the evening. For the most part, it was shown that birds actually do sing more in the morning than the evening, but that the ratio of morning song to evening song varies according to the time of year. Thus tits sing 1.6 times as much in the morning as in the evening in March and April, 2.7 times as much in May and June, and 12.8 times as much in July and August. For warblers, the same figures for the same months are 1.7, 1.6, and 24.5. The blackbird, however, is different. He consistently sings more in the evening than the morning, and during July and August does not sing in the morning at all, but only during the evening.

Another method of recording song is to time the total output of one single bird of a particular species during a complete day, or during several complete days, at different months of the year. This requires a good deal of enthusiasm and energy, for it is necessary to have practically an "all-night sitting," especially with birds like the skylark which begin to sing an hour or so before sunrise, and go on almost until sunset. In June this may mean as much as 20 hours of continuous observation, but such is the keenness of some amateur bird-watchers that this has been done, and done most effectively ! The method is to sit in the territory of one particular bird for a whole day and note the duration of its song each and every time it sings. This has been done for the skylark and willow-warbler, and the results are shown in Fig. 4. It will be seen that on May 17th this skylark sang a total of 47 minutes out of a singing day of length 13 hours 42 minutes, whilst on July 5th it sang 181 minutes for a singing day of 17 hours 55 minutes. The willow-warbler sang 75 minutes on May 17th for its singing day of length 16 hours 42 minutes, whilst on July 5th it sang only 7 minutes in a singing day of 15 hours 51 minutes. The same observer, from further data, was able to deduce that, on an average, the total output of song by the skylark, obtained by adding all the song periods together, would in one year be in the region of 7 days of 24 hours each, of continuous song. The average time for each individual song with these two birds was 2.2 *minutes* for the skylark, and 3.3 *seconds* for the willow-warbler.

These are examples of the kind of study of bird song which will yield valuable results. There is a wide field here. For example, it is commonly stated that the nightingale sings as much or even more, by day than by night, yet no accurate estimate of the ratio of time spent by this bird in day-song and night-song exists, so far as is known. We need too, accurate *quantitative* data on the effect of temperature and wind on bird song. Most bird-watchers will have noticed that birds sing much less in a high wind than in calm. Yet we know little about the relation between wind force or velocity, and volume of bird song. Again, certain birds are affected more by wind than are others. The mistle-thrush will sing in a high wind, the blackbird but rarely. If it is cold but sunny, birds will sing, but if it is cold and dark,

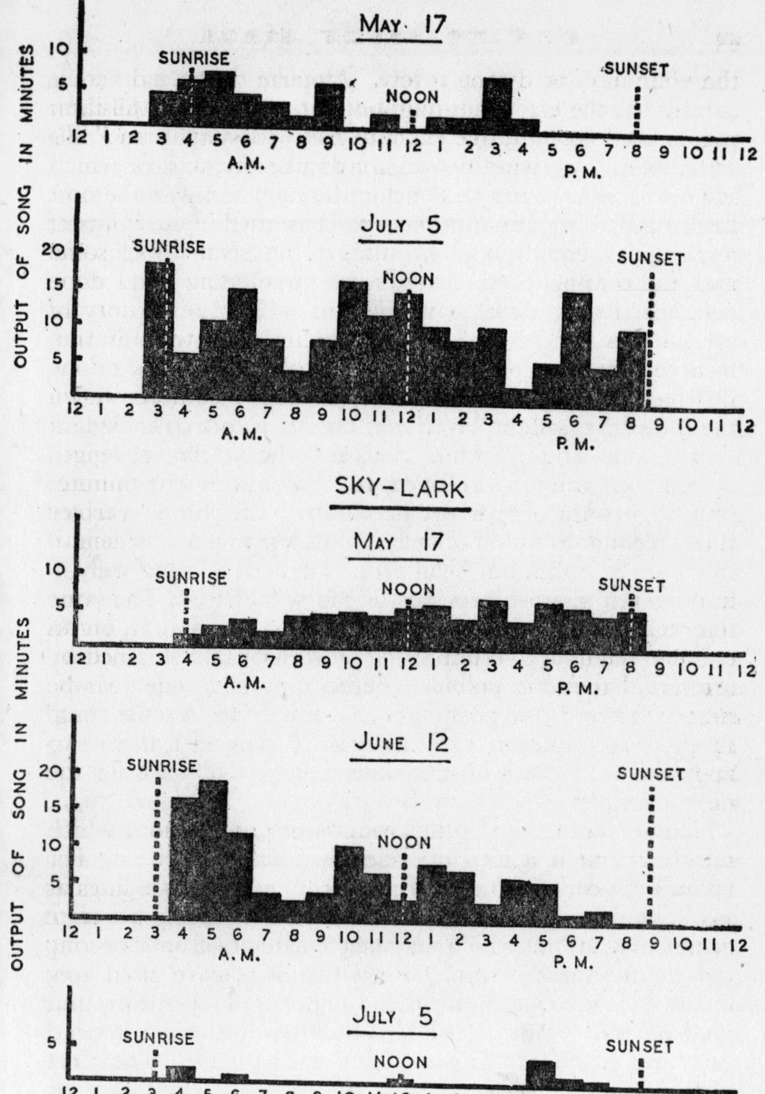


FIG. 4.—*Showing the total output of song of a skylark and a willow-warbler during a single day.*

[*After Noble Rollin*].

the volume of bird song is low. A warm west wind with a drizzle sets the birds shouting, but not a cold rain. All these points need quantitative examination with actual recording of temperatures, wind direction and velocity, and so on.

We can now return to the consideration of one of the cock birds. Let us suppose that he is safely settled in an adequate territory, defending it by shouting to his rivals to keep out and by chasing them away with threatening gestures of defiance if they dare to venture in. Here he awaits the arrival of a hen bird of his own species. But we may well be asked the question, "Why did your particular bird choose this particular spot as the best in which to settle down for the breeding season"? Such choice is often known as "habitat-selection." An obvious superficial answer is given by the fact, already referred to, that our bird is merely returning to the area where he was born and bred, and that therefore he is automatically selecting a place which is suitable, for had it not been so, his chances of being successfully reared in some previous season would have been very remote. But this answer rather begs the question for it still does not tell us *why* certain species nest in certain well-defined areas and refuse to colonise others apparently equally well suited. There is the possibility that it is bound up with food supply in some cases, but this is not a universal answer by any means. Dozens of most interesting examples exist and need careful and intimate investigation. The three pipits which nest commonly in this country are one example. The meadow-pipit is a bird of wide distribution with a typical habitat associated with moorlands, commons, rough pastures and hill sides such as chalk downs. The tree-pipit often occurs in a habitat which may be coincident with, or overlap that of, the meadow-pipit, but with this proviso, that there must be, somewhere in the vicinity of the nest, some prominent object such as a fairly tall tree or telegraph pole, from which the typical song-flight can be made. The rock-pipit has a type habitat associated with a rocky foreshore, and nests in holes between rocks. There is a high grassy cliff overlooking the sea on the Lleyn Peninsular, in Wales, where all these three-pipits breed on the one cliff; the rock-pipits at the base, the meadow pipits on the intermediate grassy area, and the tree-pipits on an area at the top of the cliff where some trees grow. To explain such a distribution is difficult merely in terms of food supply, for all the three species at one time or another obtained food from the same circumscribed area of the foreshore and the grassy cliff, with no predeliction of any one species for any one particular part. All three could sometimes be seen gathering food at the wrack of the tide marks. Hence we can only explain their distribution up this cliff in terms of a *psychological* factor influencing habitat selection. This factor probably arises from inherited memory of the type habitat and we can guess that this is a visual pattern specific to each species and involving visual " imprinting " on the bird's consciousness. Taken as a whole the visual pattern for habitat selection in the tree-pipit must be one involving a prominent tree or high post ; for the meadow-pipit probably a wide area of rough grass or heather ; and for the rock-pipit the foreshore with probably the visual pattern of the sea as an added essential.

A similar interesting case is that of the three " leaf " warblers, the chiff-chaff, willow-warbler, and wood-warbler. In Epping Forest, all three birds breed in fair numbers and in certain areas they overlap considerably, yet there is discernable a very distinct preference for a specialised habitat in the chiff-chaff and wood-warbler, whilst the willow-warbler is more cosmopolitan, and will breed almost anywhere in the forest. Thus the chiff-chaff breeds in the areas of Epping Forest where there is a mixed growth of deciduous trees which allows of plenty of undergrowth beneath them, but in such a spot one never finds the wood-warbler. A few hundred yards away, however, there may be an extensive grove of ancient beech and hornbeam, with no undergrowth at all, and here one finds the wood-warbler breeding. The willow-warbler can be found in either area and from the point of view of search for food, there is, in the contiguous areas along the two different types of habitat, a general mixing of the three species. Here again we have, apparently, a psychological differentiation of the species—the chiff-chaff with a liking for woodland *with* undergrowth, the wood-warbler with a liking for woodland *without* undergrowth, and the willow-warbler with general adaptation to either type of habitat. If a wood is modified so that undergrowth develops, the wood-warbler will desert it as a breeding-area, and its place may be taken by the chiff-chaff.

But there is little doubt also that a great many factors other than the psychological ones enter into the association of a certain species of birds with certain types of habitat, for otherwise we could not account for the fact that of two areas which apparently contain all the visual pre-requisites of the type habitat, one may be thickly populated and the other left untenanted. Thus a wood from which all the dead and decayed trees are ruthlessly removed (as they are in scientific forestry), will not have its complement of hole-nesting birds like tits, creepers, or flycatchers, whilst another wood, identical in all other respects, but from which the old and decayed trees have not been removed, has its normal tenancy of these birds. The thing missing here is a suitable nesting site, which is a direct factor and scarcely a psychological one. As suggested earlier, food too, is bound to play an important part with many birds, especially with those birds in which the food fed to the young is specialised or changes gradually as the young grow up. The kingfisher is a case in point. When the young are very small, they are fed mainly on minute fresh-water crustaceæ and small water insects. Later tadpoles, dragon-fly larvae and sometimes worms are fed to the young and finally, as they grow older, small fish, especially minnows and gudgeon complete the diet. To obtain these different foods at the different times they are needed, kingfishers work different parts of a stream, going upstream to the shallows for the first and downstream to the deeper water for the last. The nest-hole may be anywhere along the stream, the main pre-requisite being a steep bank of softish soil (often sandy loam) preferably with a slight overhanging at the top. The only psychological factor seems to be the presence of a perch near the nest-hole. When studying the types of habitat associated with certain species of birds, it is of interest to consider how far the shrinkage of such habitats, from natural or human agency, is likely to affect the status of the birds associated with them. It is obvious that a lot will depend on the ability of a particular species to adapt itself to a changing environment. If any species remains rigidly fixed in its total association with any specialised environment, then steady shrinkage of such environment will automatically mean an increasing rarity of the species concerned. The crested and bearded tits are interesting because they represent birds whose extreme rarity in this country can be explained in terms of shrinkage of highly specialised habitats. The crested tit is now mainly confined to a small area of Speyside, and it is a sedentary species which sticks closely to its specialised environment. This is the remnant of the old Caledonian pine-forest which clusters around the foothills of the Cairngorms. Following on the final retreat of the last ice-cap, this conifer forest probably stretched over most of Britain, and the crested tit was probably at this time quite common over large areas of this country, along with other birds typical of a pine and birch forest association, like the coal- and willow-tits, gold crest, and redstart. Later, the conifer forests were displaced northwards more and more by the deciduous forests of the south, and the birds associated with the conifers were left with two choices. They could either retreat along with their old type habitat, or stay put and adapt themselves to the new. The interesting thing is that while the coal-tit remained, and adapted itself to the deciduous forest (so that it is still a common bird in this country), the crested tit proved far less adaptable and, as always with animals which fail to adapt themselves to changed conditions, is now merely a remnant—a kind of feathered clan clinging to a Highland stronghold. Any further reduction in the specialised habitat, such as results from extensive felling of timber during war-time, must further imperil the already shrunken area in which the crested tit breeds.

From the ecological point of view, the bearded tit offers a similar problem. It is a bird associated with a particular type of marsh land, with sedge and reeds growing direct from a small depth of water. The drainage of the East Anglian fen country during the past few centuries reduced the bearded tit to a mere handful. But this is not all, for so delicately balanced is the ecology of this bird that certain marshes, even in an apparently favourable area of the

Norfolk Broads, will remain untenanted. It seems that the birds prefer a marsh which is not too frequently cut or mown, a growth of from two to five years being ideal. The insect life of such a marsh is, as one would expect, as specialised a type as the marsh vegetation on which it exists, and all this tends to restrict the range of the bearded tit. For this reason the inundations of the sea into the Broads in 1938 confronted these birds with a catastrophe from which they have as yet barely recovered, since the high salinity of the water killed much of the characteristic vegetation.

So we see that in selecting his area, our bird will be influenced, through a sort of sub-conscious instinct, by many physical factors, such as availability of food and nest sites, as well as by certain psychological factors, many of which we cannot explain in ecological terms ; hence, we must not let interest in the psychological ramifications of the bird's world blind us to the fact that many hard and concrete factors of its external environment do much to shape a bird's life and death.

# CHAPTER 3

## NUPTIALS AND NESTING

HAVING secured for himself a territory in which to rear a family, our cock bird, defending it vigorously, awaits the arrival of the hens. These normally come in after the cocks by a period which varies with different species, and in different years, but is usually between 9 and 15 days later. When the hen birds arrive, how precisely does this pair formation take place? We know that the hen birds will be making for the spot near to where they nested last year, so that there is a possibility, though no certainty, that the same birds may pair together, in the same spot, as did so last year, even though they have migrated in the meantime, over 3000 miles or more. But, through deaths and other causes, a cock bird is equally liable to get a new mate in his territory, though she may be one of his brood from the previous year or even a sister. Birds of one species inhabiting a given area are almost certain to be closely inter-related, and to be derived from intensive in-breeding. But contrary to popular opinion, in-breeding as such is not a bad thing. On the contrary, provided the strain is good and *no hereditary defects are present*, in-breeding coupled with rigid selection tends to improve a stock rather than otherwise, and is the method used by live-stock breeders to build up pure pedigree strains. Since, under natural wild conditions, defects are automatically eradicated by stringent natural selection, brother and sister crosses and the like would tend to strengthen rather than weaken, a group of birds of a given species.

Our cock's mate whatever her origin, will have dropped down into his territory from out of the southern sky, and with the coming of dawn, hears him begin to sing from his song-perch, and as a result of this song, she goes to seek out the cock. It is not, be it noted, the other way round, as it is with many mammals ; the cock bird does not seek the hen, but the hen, the cock bird. What happens from then on forms one of the most fascinating chapters in the study of



FIG. 5.—TWO BIRDS WITH HIGHLY SPECIALISED HABITATS: (Left) *The crested tit, confined to the ancient Caledonian pine forest.* (Right) *The bearded tit, confined to certain areas of the Norfolk Broads.*

bird-life, for the pair-formation and nuptials leading up to the production of the clutch of eggs in the nest give us whole patterns of behaviour, and interplay between the two sexes, the study of which is of fundamental importance in arriving at some understanding of the tiny mind behind the bright eye. According to the theory of sexual selection propounded by Darwin, the hen birds are most attracted to those cocks which have the finest feathers and songs, and generally are able to " show-off " to the best advantage. Therefore, said Darwin, the cock in poor voice and plumage has less chance of securing a mate than a neighbour with better plumage and song. Although there may be a certain amount of truth in this idea it seems equally probable that in many cases, provided the cock bird is physiologically in a fit state for breeding, the comparative state of his plumage and voice may play quite a secondary part in influencing the success or otherwise of his pairing. An American observer has shown from extensive studies of the song-sparrow, that the " choice" of mates may be perfectly haphazard, and that chance plays a large part in deciding which hen bird mates with a particular cock. Certainly single cock birds which attempt to intervene between two birds which are already paired up, very rarely accomplish a split, even though the intervening cock may be an altogether more brilliant bird than the paired one. In one instance, a cock yellow wagtail hatched on a Cheshire farm the previous year returned to the same area and secured a territory. He was in poor plumage, still retaining some of the markings on the sides of the head which are characteristic of the immature phase of plumage. His yellow underparts were dull and undeveloped. Yet he was vigorous in securing and defending his territory, and was sought out by a hen bird. About three days after the arrival of this hen bird, a second cock came in. He was in the most brilliant plumage, with flashing yellow breast and underparts, yet when he attempted to wrest the territory from the first cock bird, he failed completely. After two days of intense fighting, he moved elsewhere, and the cock with the poor plumage remained in possession of the territory and the hen bird. During all this time, the hen bird took not the slightest apparent interest in the proceedings. While the two cocks fought and postured and sang, she fed placidly about the territory or stood and preened herself. There was no sign of any interest in either of the cocks, or of making a choice one way or the other. When the bright plumaged cock moved on, mating between the hen and her " chosen " cock was normal, and they reared a brood on the territory. We need a great many observations similar to this in order to come to a full understanding of the circumstances under which a hen bird attaches herself to a particular cock bird. Chance enters in, but so also must biological considerations, especially the internal states of the two birds.

When the hen bird first approaches the cock in his territory, the question arises of how he recognises her. If the plumage of the two sexes is different, there is reason to believe that recognition that the bird is a hen is often made by the cock through this plumage difference. The hen may also have a characteristic call note. When the plumage of the two sexes is the same, as in the robin, it has been suggested that recognition is based on the reaction of the hen bird to threat postures. If the cock postures and the bird before him does not retreat or adopt similar threat postures back, then the cock realises that the bird before him is a hen. Such an approach to the problem of recognition amongst birds with the same plumage in the two sexes is simple, and those who watch birds closely will realise that demeanour can influence recognition a great deal. Hide tents used close to nests for observation purposes will enable the bird-watcher to see that many hen birds have a demeanour and general " attitude " which distinguish them instantly from the cock even though the plumages of the two may be identical. The hen is often to be picked out by her more " demure " attitudes, if such a word can be used. She goes more quietly about her business, usually adopts a more crouching stance on the ground, especially when in the presence of the cock, and generally lacks the aggressiveness of the male bird. But, as was stated in the discussion on threat display and its frequent similarity to nuptial display, it is probable that recognition is obtained from many factors besides posture reaction. From experiments performed in the field, it can be shown that many species in which the plumage of the two sexes is different, rely almost entirely on this difference for recognition purposes. Thus the black cock cannot be deceived by a crouching posture if a stuffed male be placed in that position in the " lek," and it will immediately attack such a dummy. If the stuffed bird is a female, however, the crouching position immediately elicits attempts at copulation. Even in birds with identical plumage, like the jackdaw, recognition by the birds themselves has been proved to be possible, merely through slight facial differences. The black-headed gull can distinguish the birds of its own little group nesting within the larger confines of the colony, and also the identity of its own mate, although no great plumage differences is apparent between the sexes. Young herring-gull chicks will also readily pick out their parents from a host of similar birds, and can even distinguish foreign chicks. Slight variations of plumage, as well as of posture and demeanour, thus undoubtedly help birds to recognise one another.

We will suppose then that a hen bird has approached our cock in his territory, and that as a result of a preliminary inspection, our cock bird seems disposed to tolerate the presence of this hen in his territory. From now on, events move forward towards the first climax of the breeding phase, that is, the completion of the egg clutch in the nest. To attain this climax, an ordered sequence of behaviour evolves in both birds, the unconscious aim of which is the bringing of their bodies into the correct condition for breeding. This is attained by a process of mutual stimulation, the part played by the hen bird varying from species to species. It has been suggested that in those birds in which the sexes are quite or almost similar, and both adorned with bright colours or special plumage characters which can be employed in display, the two sexes play almost identical roles in mutual stimulation. This is especially true of the grebes, where much of the display is so similar in both birds, that that of the female is at times practically a " mirror-image " of the male's. But it is certainly not universally true, for in the shelduck, the only British breeding duck with identical bright plumage characters in both male and female, the display follows the typical " duck-type," where the female takes little or no part beyond dipping her bill into the water. In general, amongst the smaller birds, where the male possesses plumage characters not found in the female, the part of the latter in mutual display is a minor one, at any rate from the point of view of external evidences, but there are many unelaborate postures and wing-movements on the part of such female birds which it is important to notice, and which may be easily overlooked in the study of the far more frequent and striking displays of the male. Just how rapidly our pair of birds pass from the initial contact of pairing to the full climax of mating depends on many factors, one of the chief being climatic. If the season here be backward, so that the provision of suitable nesting-sites is poor due to undeveloped herbage, or if abnormally low temperatures prevail, the passage from initial pair-formation to actual mating may be protracted. With resident birds which normally flock in winter, such as lapwings, grouse, or curlew, a spell of cold weather in early spring will often break up the pairs and the birds will reassemble again into flocks. Hence we may have, once again, psychological and physical factors affecting the rate of progress of our pair of birds towards sexual fulfilment. Leafless undergrowth or too short herbage may not present the necessary visual stimulation, which helps to regulate the urge to build a nest, and a psychologically essential factor may thus be missing; or a cold period with perhaps snow, in early spring, may affect food supplies, and thus a physical factor enters in, which retards sexual progress. Such interplay between the psychological and the physical is continually affecting the bird's life. But if the season is fairly normal, we may expect a sequence of events such as the following. For the first day or so our pair of birds will keep more or less together, the cock usually at his song-perch; with the hen somewhere nearby in the bushes or trees. They will feed together at frequent intervals, and possibly during such feeding, the cock may offer the hen food which he has found. This she receives with shimmering wings, her body in a flat crouched attitude. Later she consistently begs for food with opened beak and the same shimmered wings and crouched body, and in general appears to copy the food-begging attitudes of the young bird. She may also use the

" cheeping " note of the young bird at this time. The period of sexual stimulation through visual patterns has commenced, and from now on until final mating both birds will keep close together, and through the gradual effect of visual stimuli of ever-increasing complexity and emotional significance, will approach the climax of this first phase of the breeding cycle. Mutual stimulation towards a sexual goal has been well demonstrated from studies of the behaviour of colony-nesting birds in the breeding season. With birds like the gulls, the mutual stimulation towards sexual maturity is one, not only of the individuals of a pair for one another, but of the whole mass of birds for each individual within the mass. This has led one ornithologist to put forward a valuable concept which we can call the " mass stimulation " idea. By this, it is suggested that, for birds which nest together in large groups, a very important factor in the safety of the colony is the need for most of the eggs to be laid at approximately the same time, so that a large proportion of the adults may be incubating eggs or feeding young together, and in this way, the time during which downy chicks are exposed to predatory birds is cut to a minimum. In order that this may occur, the majority of the pairs must come to full breeding condition at the same time, and this is accomplished by the sexual excitation produced by the mass of birds in the colonial unit. Contained in this theory is also the idea that for colony-nesting birds there will be a minimum number below which the effect of mass stimulation will be so slight that the birds find it difficult to reach the sexual maturity necessary for successful breeding. As an example of the latter, the case of the fulmar petrel is often quoted. This bird which formerly nested mainly on St. Kilda, has spread during the present century in a remarkable manner, and now bids fair to reach the south coast of England. Its methods of colonising the cliffs on which it breeds have been noted, and it is usual for a preliminary inspection by one or two birds to take place in one year, to be followed by the regular presence of several non-breeding birds in the next, until finally, when a little group has collected, regular breeding commences. During the first year or so, the birds may behave as though breeding, and display to one another and show attachment to a given suitable breeding ledge, but no egg is laid. Finally the favourable physiological state is reached, and breeding commences. This concept of a minimum threshold number below which socially nesting birds find it difficult to attain successful breeding may explain too, why it is so often difficult for the remnant of a rare species of bird to re-establish itself.

Our pair of birds, being non-social in their nesting habits, will rely on the stimulation of one another. The nuptial displays which now take place have been very much studied by field ornithologists, but there is still a great deal to learn about the display of individual species. Birds make considerable use of those parts of their plumage which are highly coloured, or have prominent physical features like waving crests, or long sweeping tails which can be fanned out. Thus as a typical and interesting display, we may consider that of the redshank, which is a summer visitor to its inland breeding haunts, although it may be seen on our coasts at all seasons of the year. The birds return to their breeding haunts in the last two weeks of March, and display takes place at or near, some feeding ground in the vicinity of the nesting ground. The birds usually " flight-in " to the pools where they feed, in small groups of three or four, calling with the well-known yodelling note as they drop to earth. For about a minute after arrival, the birds stand tense and motionless in well-separated groups, but soon several of the males begin to show signs of becoming restless and excited. One commences to shiver its wings, slightly at first, but with gradually increasing vigour, and with both wings vibrating to run round one of the females, bowing and curtseying at the same time. The female often appears quite indifferent to this display, and merely stands in a hunched-up attitude without moving. The displaying bird, however, soon galvanises another male in the group to action, which launches an attack upon it (Fig. 6 A). Both birds rise into the air ; a clash occurs (Fig. 6 B); one is forced down into a pool, and the upper bird follows up his advantage by diving on to the back of the other and ducking it under the surface (Fig. 6 C). This bird then returns to the female and takes up a position behind her, with raised and vibrating wings. The female looks round once or twice, but otherwise makes no recognition of the display (Fig. 6 D). The male bird then goes round to the front of the female and approaches her with a slow mincing gait, deliberately picking his way. The wings are then raised right above the back, and the head bowed until the beak touches the ground. Next the tips of the wings begin to tremble, which shivering motion is extended until the whole of the wings are shaking violently. In this way the gleaming white undersides are effectively displayed to the female (Fig. 6 E). At the same time, the male bird "marks time" rapidly with his red legs, then rises into the air and hangs hovering over the female, calling loudly all the time (Fig. 6 F). He then ceases to call, and descends towards her in short sliding movements, with red legs dangling and wings still shivering violently, and finally alights on the back of the female. (Fig. 6 G). If the time be opportune and the hen has adopted a crouching stance, coition then normally takes place; otherwise the female moves forward and the male flutters to the ground. Finally he bows round the female with fanned tail (Fig. 6 H).

There are a great many similarly interesting and beautiful nuptial displays for the student to watch and record. Yellow wagtails puff out their bright yellow breast feathers and also hover over the female. Most of those birds without bright colours use instead their intricate feather patterning for display. Thus many of the waders employ their variegated feather patterns in display, lacking as they do any brightly coloured ornaments. In this connection it is interesting to note the probability that the actions and postures used in display are older, from an evolutionary point of view, than are the ornaments and colours brought into play by the posturing. For instance many ducks of different species employ similar postures for display, yet while in some species these postures happen to accentuate certain highly coloured parts of the bird's body, in others the same parts may not be strikingly coloured at all. The dabchick and the great crested grebe have similar displays involving neck and head, yet the former has no "ruff," which is such a prominent feature of the latter's display. A more remarkable case is

A FIG. 6.—AGGRESSIVE AND NUPTIAL DISPLAYS OF THE REDSHANK.
*One cock bird commences to display to the hen, while the second rushes to attack.*

B *The two cocks fight in mid-air.*

C *One is forced down into the water.*

D *The victor returns to the hen and recommences the display with raised wings and bowed head.*

E *The cock vibrates his wings, "marks time" rapidly with his legs, and slowly approaches the hen.*

F *The cock rises into the air, and hangs over the hen, calling loudly.*

EB

G *He alights on her back.*

H *He bows round the hen, with fanned tail.*

that of pigeons which by artificial selection, can be bred without feathers and yet will go through all the postures of normally displaying pigeons, trying to use feathers that they do not even possess !

It must not be thought that the complete displays take place regularly, and that day after day the cock bird completes before the hen a set series of movements, wing-quivering, tail-fanning, and so on, until she reaches the correct state for copulation. The build-up is more gradual than that, and it is the exception rather than the rule for the ordinary bird-watcher, whose bird-watching must of necessity be somewhat casual, to witness the complete display in any species of bird. We often see *parts* of the display, for until the critical moment arrives, the cock may commence display and be incapable of finishing it because the time is not yet ripe. This incomplete performance has definite survival value, as otherwise the bird would probably exhaust itself emotionally before the hen was ready. However, as we watch, we come to realise that by degrees the hen is responding in her own particular way, which may be more or less apparent according to the species. With some birds such as the bullfinch, the female takes an active part, the courtship being largely a mutual performance. With the barn-owl, both birds will rub the sides of their facial discs together and the hen bird seems as active in displaying and mutual stimulation as is the cock. But in general the hen's part is more or less a passive one, her main reactions being a crouching posture, often with shimmering wings, which invites the male to copulate with her. As with the cock bird, her invitation display may not be a complete one, unless and until the physiological peak is reached at the same time by both birds. It is usually when the male's full display elicits the complete invitation reaction of the female that successful copulation occurs, although many attempts at mating will often take place prior to this.

Behind all this preparation for the finale which culminates in the fertilisation of the hen bird, there lies the need for the provision of a nest in which to deposit the eggs. Not that the birds themselves have any conscious appreciation of a goal at which they are aiming in this, or for that matter in any, sequence of behaviour on which they embark. The biological end to which all these instinctive actions are leading may be wholly apparent to the human observer, but there is little evidence for the view that any of the bird's actions can be interpreted as purposive behaviour. Man is capable of ordering his actions towards a preconceived end, but birds cannot do so. Contemporary therefore with the period of nuptial display, there exists the instinctive desire to build a complete nest, and this desire increases with the progress towards the mating climax. We say " complete nest " because in some birds, the cock may begin the nest before pairing has been achieved, the hen bird then finishing it off. This happens particularly with such birds as the common and lesser whitethroats, whilst the male common wren may also build a number of " cock's nests," one of which will generally be lined and used for breeding by the hen with which he pairs.

Which of the two birds chooses the nest-site, and what share each of them takes in the actual construction of the nest are subjects worthy of close attention, for although we know a little about a fair number of species in this respect, the accounts are still rather scanty. Such records as have been published have recently been collected together, but much still remains to be done. As always, when confronted with incomplete data, we find numerous complexing anomalies. Thus in some resident birds (e.g. starling, tree-sparrow and some of the tits) actual nest-site selection may have taken place as long as two months before building begins ; in others like the migrant pied fly-catcher, willow-warbler and redstart, the cock may choose the site before the arrival of the hens, although in none of these three species will he subsequently take much part in the actual construction of the nest. In other birds again, like the two thrushes and the blackbird, the hen birds will often crouch in the bare fork of a tree, or upon selected branches, on several days prior to building. The male lapwing can be seen in early spring making the well-known "scrapes." The formation of these seems a part of the nuptials of this bird, for he often makes them before the female, by leaning forward with his breast touching the ground, feathers puffed out, and hind parts raised. The bird then shuffles round on the ground, first one way and then the other, whilst the feet, working alternately, scrape out the soil in a backwards direction. Usually the hen lapwing will choose one of these scrapes and line it with a few grasses. In many of the smaller passerine birds, the hen seems to choose the actual nest-site, often by continually flying down towards the chosen spot, crouching on it for a moment, and then flying up again. This is true of the three pipits which breed here, and hen buntings also adopt similar measures. The cock birds may, or may not, be in attendance. In the case of a pair of whin-chats, the hen bird dropped repeatedly from a perch to a tuft of grass and back again, and it was beneath this tuft that the nest was finally constructed. How long after the site is selected the actual construction of the nest itself commences, depends on a variety of factors. It may range from two months to several hours. What *is* certain is that the urge to construct the nest mounts as sexual maturity approaches, and after copulation, the nest is often finished in a great burst of energy if it is not already complete.

We come now to a consideration of the role of the sexes in the actual construction of the nest. It is a remarkable fact that very few people, even keen field ornithologists, have actually watched the complete construction of a bird's nest. For one thing, it is often impossible, without disturbing a bird, to get a really good view of the intricate and rapid actions which are employed in nest construction, especially as the birds are often hidden in dense foliage. As far as the share of cock and hen is concerned, birds can be conveniently divided into four categories, namely:

(1) Species in which both sexes build.
  (*a*) Species in which both take full and equal share.
  (*b*) Species in which the male builds a so-called "cock's nest" and the female lines it afterwards.

(2) Species in which the female alone builds and the male alone finds the materials.

(3) Species in which the female both gathers the material and builds the nest, the male taking no active part.

(4) Species in which the female alone builds but both provide material.

Considering these categories in turn we have under 1 (*a*), in which both take full and equal share, such birds as the long-tailed tit, where both birds seem equally capable of doing any or all of the intricate parts of nest-construction. Under 1 (*b*) where the cock provides nests for the hen to line, we have as examples the two whitethroats and the common wren. Category (2), where the female alone builds and the male alone brings the materials, is exemplified by the wood-pigeon ; Category (3) with the male taking no active part, by the goldfinch, greenfinch and bullfinch, the two thrushes and the blackbird, chats, warblers, tits and many other birds. This class is by far the largest and it is obvious that it is the general rule for the hen bird to be the main creator of the nest. Finally under category (4), we have birds like the magpie where the cock and hen both bring materials to the nest-site, but only the hen can construct. Ravens, rooks and choughs also belong to this category. It will be noted in studying these four main categories that there is no single one in which the hen bird does not take at least an equal share in the nest construction and usually she has the main fashioning of the nest. Even in those abnormal species in which the cock bird does all the incubating, like the phalaropes and the dotterel, the hen helps with the construction of the rudimentary nest.

The actual materials used in the construction of birds' nests naturally vary widely from species to species, but the extent to which mud is employed is not generally appreciated. The case of the mud-lined nest of the song-thrush is well known, but many other birds employ mud both as internal consolidation, and as an external foundation. Thus most of the crow family use a mixture of mud and sticks for the basic foundation of the nest. The magpie's deep, domed nest is beautifully constructed by the hen bird by interweaving sticks and filling in the spaces with mud and earth mixed with small stones. Thus these birds were employing the principle of reinforcing their " concrete," thousands of years before men thought of it. The thrushes too also employ mud and moist earth quite lavishly. The song-thrush's nest is similar in basic construction to those of the mistle-thrush and blackbird, since all make a foundation of stout grasses mixed with mud. The linings differ, however, for while the song-thrush has a thin layer of dung or rotten wood mixed with saliva, as lining, the blackbird whilst retaining a mud lining, finishes by adding dead grasses. The mistle-thrush has the same basis of mud for foundation as have the song-thrush and blackbird but does not have a mud lining, since it finishes with moss and then dead grasses. The kittiwake, breeding on open ledges on the face of steep sea-cliffs, makes an initial foundation on the rock by mixing mud and weeds together and treading the mixture into the irregular rock surface. The nest is then constructed on this base. Nuthatches plaster the entrance of their nest-holes with mud until they are just the correct size ; the dipper stiffens the " doorstep " entrance to its nest with mud, whilst the most extensive use to which it is put by any group of birds is in the all-mud nests of the *hirundinidae* (swallow family). Perhaps the most wonderful nest in this country from a construction point of view is that of the long-tailed tit. This is achieved by the extensive use of spider-silk or cocoon silk, which is to be found on the trunks of trees and in crevices of walls. The spider silk is interwoven in a marvellous way with moss as the main foundation, and a layer of lichen and cobwebs added for the exterior. Up to 2000 feathers may be added as lining. The delicate interweaving of the fine strands of spider silk, each well under one-thousandth of an inch in diameter, with pieces of moss and lichen, and its felting together into a homogeneous whole by the action of the birds' bodies, remains the most perfect example of the nest-building art.

As the nest begins to grow it is continually shaped inside by the actions of the hen, who gyrates round and round within the cup of the nest, moulding it to her body. In this way, the shape and dimensions of the final cup are automatically adjusted. There is a great deal of variation between different species with regard to complexity in nest construction, and it seems that certain species have progressed further in this respect than others. Often too, a bird, owing to lack of suitable nesting sites, or sometimes for no apparent reason at all, will choose a site quite unsuited to the type of nest it constructs. Under these circumstances the bird is unable to adapt its nest to the unusual surroundings, and builds one differing in no respect from the one it would have constructed in a typical site. Such nests are quite unsuited to their environment and often come to grief. When song-thrushes are deprived of bushes and undergrowth, they sometimes nest on the ground under vegetables, nettles, or in tall grasses. The nests are just " dumped " on the ground without any anchoring and can be picked up as a whole without damage to their foundations. Such a nest is shown in Fig. 7, placed on the bare ground beneath a cauliflower ! Again, when birds adopt nesting-sites which are not natural ones, they are often led completely astray if the site chosen offers a series of visual patterns which repeat at frequent intervals. Such sites may be the rungs of a ladder hanging against a wall, the girders of a metal bridge, walls with bricks regularly missing—as they often are when it is intended to build against the wall at some future date—and similar man-made sites. Under such circumstances a bird choosing to place its nest in one of the cavities may be utterly confused by the fact that identical cavities exist close to the original one, and the bird will often fill dozens of the holes with partially constructed nests before finally finishing one. Thus, in one case, a blackbird chose as a nest-site a corner of one of the square openings made by the rungs and side of a ladder hanging against a wall. The bird commenced a nest in the angle of one of the openings, but was so baffled by the similarity of the successive openings that it laid nest-foundations in every one of them. Later it attempted to build up three of the foundations and finally made only a rudimentary cup in one of the nests. This was never finished, since it is probable that the extended time taken by the bird to get to that stage meant that a large amount of physical energy was expended and much emotional confusion produced which finally exhausted the bird so that it could not complete the sequence of building operations. Similar confusion, with its attendant multiple nest construction, may be seen in pied wagtails which often build in holes in brick structures, like sewage farm settling tanks. Such examples rarely, if ever, occur under natural conditions, however, since similar exact resemblances do not then exist, but only in artificial man-made structures. They offer striking proof of the dominance of the visual pattern in the bird's world, and also of the fact that the random variety of natural patterns has obviated the need for highly intelligent behaviour in birds. In most cases it is perfectly safe for the bird to have an automatic response when presented with a given visual pattern, since disorder and variability lie inherent in the natural background of a bird's existence, and it is highly improbable that it will be presented with identical visual stimuli in two places sufficiently close together in time and space to cause confusion. The same confusion exists, again under artificial conditions, when a nest is moved from its original position, even though the displacement is comparatively small. Sometimes a nest in a hole in a tree has been lowered by cutting the branch, or a nest-box removed and nailed in a somewhat different position. Invariably the bird returns to the *exact* spot which the nest originally occupied, although in the case of the lowered branch this may be a spot in mid-air. The bird hovers, bewildered, before the empty space in air where the nest-hole previously was, or in the case of the moved nest-box, will cling to the trunk at the old spot. This takes place even though the nest hole is readily visible in its new position, the distance possibly being only a foot or so. It takes the bird some little time, and often several fresh visits to the site, to adapt itself to the changed conditions, so rigidly inter-knit are the intimate details of the visual patterns dominating its behaviour.

It was mentioned earlier in this chapter that few bird-watchers had, as yet, recorded the methods by which individual species construct their nests from the laying of the foundations to the final lining, but recently, this has been done for the tree-creeper. In this instance, the birds chose to build in a woodshed, in a corner made by two upright posts with bark still on them, and a roughcast wall. The very first material brought was a fine white thread-like material which turned out to be long threads of mycelium from fungi growing on tree-trunks nearby. This was collected by the hen bird who wound them round her bill into a little bunch and then worked them into the bark of the corner posts, and into the roughcast of the wall. In this way a sort of tangled matting foundation was laid. Into this were worked fine twigs of birch, mountain ash and larch, which were laid across the intervening space between the two posts to make a kind of platform, whilst others were laid across these with their ends worked into the matted foundation on the roughcast. Thereafter the twigs were laid irregularly until the main mass of the nest was formed. In order to make the cup, the bird crouched on the top of the mass of twigs and added to the structure all round herself, building it up and retaining a hollow by reason of the presence of her body. Finally she finished with some threads from coconut door matting and wool from some old rugs ! The feather-lining was composed of soft feathers from the breast of a bullfinch.

As far as pairing and mating of birds is concerned, there remains to be considered the question of polygamy and polyandry. Until recently, it was generally considered that the majority of birds were strict monogamists, and that only very specialised types departed from this rule. While this may still be mainly true, it is significant that recent careful and intensive field-work has tended to reveal that certain birds thought previously to breed in single pairs often show distinct polygamy. The corn-bunting is one such bird, for observations on its breeding biology have shown that the hen birds usually far outnumber the cocks. In one area, forty-five nesting hens were mated to only twenty-four cocks, of which fifteen were definitely proved to be polygamous. The same observer was able to show, in the same area but in a different year, that four cock corn-buntings owned two hens each, seven owned three hens each, two owned four hens each, and two cocks were actually paired with seven hens each. Thus fifteen male corn-buntings were mated to fifty-one hen birds ! There is little doubt that similar work amongst other birds would reveal equally striking departures from the general rule of monogamy. The harriers are birds in which one cock is frequently paired with two hens, bigamy in both montagu's harrier and the marsh-harrier having been noted. Two cases of bigamy in the robin have been

FIG. 7.—*Unusual nest of song-thrush, under a cut cauliflower.*

recorded and cases of polygamy in the common wren, redshank and eiderduck are on record. In contrast with these, we have the cases of polyandry, where one hen bird is mated with several cocks. It is probable that the cuckoo is often polyandrous and that the dozen or more eggs laid by a hen cuckoo in one season may have been fertilised by more than one cock bird. Quite frequently, nests of various species of birds are found with abnormally large clutches of eggs, for example, a great tit's nest with twelve eggs, a partridge's with twenty-eight, a linnet's with ten and so on. These abnormally large clutches are usually the work of two females, but whether they are mated to the same male bird or not is rarely, if ever, noted. Much work remains to be done on the ratio of the sexes during the breeding phase, with different species of birds. Why should the corn-bunting tend to be polygamous? Is it just a chance that the ratio of the sexes of these birds in a given area forces polygamy upon them, or is it a widespread and constant habit regardless of their numbers? At present we do not know, but it seems probable that the polygamy would not exist if there were enough cock birds to go round.

# CHAPTER 4

## THE EGG, AND THE YOUNG BIRD

Our birds have now completed a definite stage in their breeding cycle. The perils of the migratory journey have been avoided or overcome ; successful pairing and mating has taken place ; and a nest stands completed and awaiting the deposition by the hen bird of the first egg of the clutch. We have seen how the external environment of the birds has, mainly through visual stimili, brought their bodies towards the correct state for breeding. As this state approaches, the rudimentary eggs within the ovary begin to develop, and they steadily enlarge and commence to absorb yolk. Development continues and the rudimentary eggs pass towards and into the oviduct where they are finally fertilised by the male sperms. Thereafter processes along the oviduct deposit the albumin (egg-white), a soft skin of keratin (which is the same substance as feathers are composed of), and finally the hard chalky shell, which is white or pigmented according to the species of bird. The egg is laid by the hen bird broad-end first. Normally a whole string of rudimentary eggs is produced in the hen bird and there are usually many more to be found in the oviduct than are represented by the normal clutch of the bird. The interesting question then arises, " Why is it that there is a normal number of eggs in the clutch of any one species, which it is unusual for a bird of that species to exceed ? " The actual number of eggs in the clutch of different species varies enormously, from the single egg of the guillemot, laid on the bare ledge of a sea-cliff, to the fifteen to twenty laid by the partridge. It is possible that the number of eggs in the clutch is correlated with the mortality rate of the species, since a subtle balance must necessarily be set up if the species is to survive at a given strength in numbers, but such adjustment can only take place over periods of evolutionary time, and the idea that game birds have large clutches because their mortality rate is high from artificial causes due to shooting, represents far too narrow an attitude. What has been definitely proved however, is that birds tend to have bigger clutches in the northern part of their breeding range than in the southern part. This is very probably due to the added hours of daylight in higher latitudes, which give the adult bird a longer time in which to search for food for the young, and thus increase somewhat the chances of the successful rearing of a slightly larger brood. We have remarked that normally, when the hen bird has completed her clutch, she stops laying, and proceeds to incubate the eggs until they are successfully hatched. As we have seen, this does not mean that the hen bird produces within her body just that number of rudimentary eggs which are represented by the normal clutch, and no more. On the contrary, many more eggs are produced within the hen bird's ovary, but they are re-absorbed as soon as the clutch is complete. There must, therefore, be some controlling factor which inhibits egg-laying when the complete clutch has been produced, and once again, the answer probably lies in an inherited visual pattern of an egg-clutch of a given size. If this be so, then consistent removal of an egg from an uncompleted clutch ought to force the female bird to go on laying for a prolonged period, in an effort to make up the appropriate number of eggs demanded by the clutch-pattern. That this actually happens is, of course, well known, since the methods of egg-collectors were bound to demonstrate it time and again. Hundreds of examples exist of cases where birds have laid double or treble the normal number of eggs, when an egg is consistently removed each time, and in a certain case, as many as seventy-one eggs, laid in seventy-three days were recorded. We do not yet know, however, whether it is possible to get all species of birds to go on producing eggs in an effort to complete the egg-clutch, but there is little doubt that the majority of birds will do so. Once again, one has to be on guard against too rigid an attitude, for sometimes, under quite natural conditions and for no apparent reason, a hen bird will lay a clutch which falls short of the normal number. In addition, once incubation has actually started, removal of an egg does not invoke a renewal of egg-laying. The physical response to any external visual pattern is only complete if the internal physiological state is exactly tuned to that visual stimulus, and the phases through which the bird passes during the breeding season tend to be so distinct that a visual pattern which one day invokes a normal response will the next quite fail to do so if the bird has meantime passed on to another stage in the cycle. Thus the mere onset of the incubation phase in the hen bird following completion of the clutch prevents further laying, and eggs can be removed from the clutch without re-invoking the egg-laying phase. The power of the clutch pattern as a visual stimulus has gone and only if the bird deserts the nest, and recommences the cycle right from the beginning with a new nest, will she normally produce more eggs.

Although many experiments by collectors have demonstrated that birds strive consistently to complete a normal clutch-pattern, the reverse experiment, where eggs are added to a nest and the clutch is thus finished artificially, has scarcely been tried at all. Theoretically, if the stimulus to lay is governed solely by a visual pattern composed of a given fixed number of eggs then completion of the clutch by artificial addition of eggs ought to inhibit laying in the hen bird. Whether it does so or not, is not known, and experiments along these lines might lead to interesting results.

How frequently the female bird lays her eggs, and when she starts truly to incubate them, varies with different species of birds. Thus with many of the smaller song birds, an egg is laid on each successive day, and incubation only commences with the completion of the full clutch. Under these conditions, the young birds hatch within a few hours of one another. With many birds of prey, however, the eggs are laid at intervals of two to three days, and incubation often commences not with the last egg, but at some stage intermediate between the first and last. As a result, the young do not all hatch at the same time, but at intervals which may be spread over several days. We thus find that in many owls, harriers, hawks and eagles, the young are graded in size, there being usually a very distinct difference between the largest and smallest members of the brood. This difference

is often so much to the detriment of the smallest chick in the struggle for food brought to the nest, that it succumbs. It is by no means clear why the birds of prey have evolved this habit, which is clearly antagonistic to the successful rearing of the complete brood.

We will suppose now, that our hen bird has completed her clutch of eggs and is settling down to incubate them until they finally hatch out. The question then arises concerning the share of the sexes in incubation. It has long been known that in some species the female bird does all the incubating; in others both male and female share it between them; whilst in one or two species (phalaropes and dotterel) the male bird hatches out the eggs by himself. It is not generally realised that, in the period prior to incubation, a bird undergoes definite physiological changes which result in a modification of the feathered areas which will subsequently be in the most intimate contact with the eggs. Thus "brood-spots" develop on the breast and under-parts which are patches where the feathers are temporarily moulted. The reason for this is that feathers are necessarily poor conductors of heat—their main function is to act as insulators to the very warm bodies of birds—and hence they would tend to keep the heat of the bird's body from reaching the eggs. Hence the "brood spots" are adaptations to ensure that the closest possible contact is made between the eggs and the warm surface of the bird's body. It has also been established experimentally that the areas of skin laid bare in the brood spots are at an appreciably higher temperature than the rest of the body surface, since the skin there is inflamed and red from an increased blood supply. All this helps to maintain a constant supply of heat at an adequate temperature to the developing embryo within the egg. The number of brood spots which develop varies with different birds, for in some types, such as the song birds, birds of prey, grebes and pigeons, there is a single median brood spot. The waders and gulls, however, have three such patches, two together in front, and a single one centrally behind the first two. But once again we find the inevitable anomalies, since we find that certain birds develop no brood spots at all, for the cormorants and gannets successfully hatch their eggs without

FIG. 8.—(Top) *Hen greenshank brooding empty egg-shells, whilst holding one in readiness for removal.*
(Bottom) *Hen greenshank removing egg-shell from nest.*

them. It seems certain, however, that in the majority of birds, brood spots are an important factor in incubation. The share of the sexes in incubation and the development or otherwise of brood spots in the separate sexes now becomes an important consideration. Interest in this matter has recently been increased by a suggestion that the mere presence of a male bird on the nest should not necessarily be taken to mean that the bird is incubating the eggs in the sense that it is contributing to the development of the embryo. Thus in certain cases, such as the blackbird, where the hen bird normally does all the incubation, it has been found that in isolated cases where the cock bird has been found covering the eggs, these were quite cold when the bird was flushed from the nest. No brood spots are developed by the cock blackbird, and the suggestion is that such birds are incapable of truly incubating eggs, and that the covering of the eggs should rather be described as "casual brooding." There are, of course, many species where the cock bird regularly takes a share in incubation, such cases being those where regular changes with the mate and prolonged periods on the nest, obviously indicate true incubation. There is here a wide field for further study. It seems fairly certain that in most of the warblers, thrushes, chats, buntings and finches, the male does not truly incubate, and records of the male on the nest should not be treated as necessarily indicative of incubation. The advantage of a change-over between the sexes during the incubation period is obviously connected with the getting of an adequate amount of food by each bird, and when the hen bird undertakes all the incubation, it is often the case that she is fed on the nest by the cock—though this is by no means universal. Thus in the raven, rook, magpie, chough, greenfinch and all the harriers, the food is entirely provided for the nesting hen by the male. In the goldfinch, bullfinch, chaffinch, most of the tits, the tree-creeper, and the robin, the male provides most of the food required by the incubating hen bird, but the hen occasionally leaves the nest to obtain food for herself. In certain cases, however, the hen has to fend for herself as best she may, during short periods away from the eggs, and this is the case with the larks, pipits, some warblers (chiff-chaff, willow-warbler and wood-warbler) and the hedge-sparrow. Other species remain to be worked out.

Certain birds have been carefully studied to determine the share of the sexes in incubation. In the American song-sparrow, the female alone incubates, sitting for about twenty-five minutes, then leaving to feed for about seven, and then returning. In the fulmar petrel, each sex normally incubates for four days and four nights and then is relieved by the other. The hen yellow wagtail incubates for about three-quarters of the total daylight hours and the cock for the remaining quarter. The hen apparently does all the incubation at night in this species. Where both cock and hen birds share the incubation it is of interest to note the method whereby the change-over is effected. This varies from species to species. Sometimes, as with the waders, whose nests, being in the open, provide the sitting bird with a wide field of view, the incubating bird will quietly leave when the "relief" appears in the distance, and will slink away with a crouching, hunched-up attitude. The relieving bird then cautiously approaches, often by short runs on a zigzag route, and sidles on to the nest. Birds which nest in deep cover, on the other hand, often change over at the actual nest site ; others, again, call one another off the nest from a distance.

Just as there is an instinctive urge to complete the clutch-pattern, so there is an equally strong urge to brood the clutch within the nest. Recently this "broodiness" has been shown to be associated with the secretion into the blood stream of a hormone called "prolactin" by the pituitary gland, and it is possible that, with further advance in our knowledge of the ductless gland or "endocrine" system in birds, many of the distinct phases through which birds progress during the breeding cycle will be proved to be associated with specific hormone secretion. After the onset of "broodiness" it is no exaggeration to say that birds can be induced to sit on anything ; not only objects shaped like eggs, but practically any solid object. A black-headed gull brooded a tin lid placed in its nest, whilst other birds have covered stones, pieces of wood, golf balls, and in one case, that of a starling nesting under eaves, the knuckles of a man's clenched hand held in the nest. Once again the lack of truly intelligent behaviour is only too apparent.

The temperature under incubating birds has been carefully studied in America by placing a delicate temperature-recorder known as a thermo-couple, within an egg, and taking readings at a distance from the nest, on an appropriate galvanometer attached by wires to the thermo-couple. Under these conditions, 37 species of birds of 11 different orders gave an *average* egg temperature of 93.2° F., the average for when the bird was sitting being 93.7° F., and when the bird was off the nest 92.1° F. Such a temperature within the egg is induced by a skin temperature in the sitting bird of not less than 107.6° F. Whilst the necessity for the eggs to be kept consistently warm most of the time is obvious, it is surprising how low a temperature a developing embryo will stand without succumbing. Embryos at all stages of development can be subjected to temperatures as low as 60.0° F. to 70.0° F., for as long as 16 hours without being killed, although development may be somewhat retarded, and the vitality of the hatched chick, low.

The period of incubation varies with different classes of birds. With many of the smaller passerine birds it is usually of the order of 14 days, though there are naturally variations on either side of this period ; many waders (lapwing, sandpipers, snipes, woodcock, etc.) sit from 21 days to 28 days ; ducks and geese from 28 to 35 days ; the hawks up to 35 days, the golden eagle 45 days, whilst petrels and shearwaters incubate for as long as 50 days. Just as the hen bird strives to complete the egg pattern of the complete clutch, so an incubating bird will continue diligently to sit on the eggs until the young hatch out. The only release from the instinct to brood is the appearance of the young, and if for some reason such as infertility in the eggs, these fail to appear, the birds will sit for phenomenally long periods, until physical exhaustion alone brings the process to an end. There are many examples to be found of extended periods of incubation when the clutch fails for some reason to hatch. In one case, a herring gull brooded an infertile clutch for nine weeks. Another, most abnormal case, was that of a hen blackbird which " adopted " a single mallard's egg, laid in a nest built in the fork of a low tree over water, and brooded it for seventeen days before the egg was taken, probably by a crow. The bird would no doubt have gone on incubating this strange egg for much longer had it not been taken.

Normally, however, after the requisite incubation period, the eggs begin to " chip " and the small chick within the egg can be heard trying to force its way out from within. At this moment, there is little doubt that a tremendous psychological change begins to come over the incubating bird. We have seen that the urge to incubate is very strong as soon as the egg pattern is completed, and that this will continue to be strong even over long periods of time provided the eggs do not hatch. But at the moment of hatching, it is obvious that the incubation urge has to be replaced by a new, and fundamentally different one, namely that to feed and tend the young. In most birds, the actual period of the hatch is less than two days, and so the psychological changes involved must be comparatively sudden and more or less irreversible. From studying birds in the field, we know that the emotional pitch attained at the moment of the hatch is often very high indeed. Thus the cock common partridge becomes wild with excitement when he first sees the newly hatched chicks, and a pair of song thrushes stood watching the hatch of the last egg of their clutch with such rapt attention that they allowed an observer to place his hand on the edge of the nest. Some parent birds have quite distinctive cries which are exclusively used during the hatch.

An interesting facet of this " hatching complex " is the disposal of the broken egg shells left in the nest, for after the hatch the egg shell becomes redundant, and tends rapidly to lose its significance for the bird as an integral part of its world. This being so, it is natural that the bird should dispose of the remains of the shells, and this in its turn can have survival value, since such remnants lying around the nest would tend to attract the attention of predatory birds and mammals. Just how quickly the urge to incubate loses its force appears to vary with different birds. Some will immediately set about disposing of the broken shells ; others again will seem in "two minds" for an hour or so, alternately tending the chicks and brooding the egg-shells, before finally disposing of them; whilst in a few cases the desire to incubate may persist so strongly that the bird will go on incubating for many hours. Thus in the case of the hen greenshank shown in Fig. 8 A, the bird retrieved the halves of the broken shells in her bill and actually placed them beneath her body in the brooding position. She then sat on them for a further 10 hours before the incubation urge finally subsided. Other greenshanks, on the other hand, removed shells within a few minutes of their hatching, picking them up in the bill and flying away with them from the area of the nest (Fig. 8 B). The methods of disposing of the shells varies greatly with individual birds. Many pick them up and fly away, dropping the shells at an appropriate distance from the nest. Others again, may crush the shells and eat the pieces, or may pulverise them, and stamp them into the lining of the nest. It is curious that addled eggs, on the contrary, are often left in the nest and no attempt is made to remove them after the rest of the eggs have hatched. There is consequently considerable evidence that a broken or damaged egg shell has a particular significance for the sitting bird, and stimulates a desire in the bird to remove it, and although an egg damaged early in the incubation period will sometimes cause the bird to desert the nest, it is frequently the case that the bird will remove or even eat such an egg, and then continue to incubate and hatch out the rest of the clutch.

As soon as the incubation desire has subsided, the adult birds settle down to the business of tending the young. There are two absolute essentials as far as the successful existence of the young birds is concerned, and they are warmth and an ample supply of food. Hence the young must be frequently brooded beneath the warm body of the adult bird, and at the same time kept adequately supplied with food. This applies especially to those birds whose young are born naked, helpless and blind (the so-called *nidicolous* birds), though it is also true to a certain extent of those birds whose young are born strong, with plenty of down, and able to run within a few hours of the hatch (the *nidifugous* birds).

Thus in a cold and wet breeding season we find many chicks dead in the shell and many dead chicks, for if the young are exposed to the atmosphere when the temperature falls to 50° F., they collapse rapidly especially during the first two days after birth. Young birds tend to lose heat quickly when not brooded, and their temperature drops then by several degrees. Their temperature also varies consistently with that of the atmosphere during the first few days, until down-growth advances. In addition, the amount of food necessary to keep a young bird going is at times phenomenal. It has been proved experimentally that during the first few days after its birth, the quantity of food a young starling takes each day is equal to half its own weight, and that, after the first few days, it rises to six-sevenths of its weight ! Thus six young starlings, eight days old, took ten ounces of insects in a day. When one considers the low weight of the insect prey, one gains a good idea of the immense amount of labour, and passing to and fro, which such an accumulation demands. When feeding its young, the tiny goldcrest may make twelve to twenty-four trips an hour, or 310 a day. Crested tits will usually visit their young with food every quarter of an hour in the early morning, are then less active over the midday period, but quicken to quarter-hour periods later in the afternoon. With the tree-sparrow, the young are fed during the first few days from three to four times an hour, but later, as the young grow, it may be as frequent as sixteen times an hour. This constant feeding of the young gains added point when it is realised that in the adult passerine birds, digestion is so rapid that a full stomach is entirely digested within 2½ hours. House-sparrows kept without food lose up to 4 per cent of their weight in as short a time as two hours, and the same bird is unable to endure for 24 hours *without food*, an air temperature below freezing point. There is thus a very subtle balance between external temperature and internal metabolic rate, with birds, and lack of food even for an hour or so renders birds utterly incapable of withstanding low temperatures.

In both the duty of keeping the young warm by brooding them, and of maintaining them through an adequate food supply, the cock bird usually plays a much more consistent part than he does in the construction of the nest and the incubation of the eggs. In many species where the cock does not incubate the eggs, he will none-the-less brood the young, and apart from the ducks there can be few birds in which the male does not help in tending the young. In the harriers, he seems to be the main forager, and the hen merely receives the food (usually in mid-air by way of the well-known " pass "), and takes it back to the nest.

Just as certain visual patterns appear to exercise a rigid control over the reactions of the bird during the breeding phase up to the hatching of the young, so, with the appearance of the young, new visual stimuli appear which elicit the reactions of brooding, feeding, nest-cleaning, and leading to safety, on the part of the parent birds. The chief stimulus to feed the young undoubtedly comes from the visual pattern afforded by the open beaks of the young birds, and this is often highly accentuated by the bright colours with which the palates and flanges of the gapes are furnished. The tongues of the young birds are also often adorned with bright or dark spots to accentuate the general pattern. Some of the most remarkable of such palate markings are to be found in the mouths of young bearded tits. As shown in Fig. 9 these consist of four rows of white, conical, peg-like projections, two rows on either side of the middle line and these are set in a background of black surrounded by rich carnelian-red. The palate of the nestling starling is a bright lemon-yellow, and the edge of the gape is bright yellow too. Most nestling buntings have mouths the insides of which are rose or carmine red in colour, with the gapes bright yellow ; the mouths of young tits show clearly the yellow or pale rose of their palates even in the dark recesses of the nesting holes. These bright colours may aid the parent birds in placing the food in the mouths of the young birds when the nest is in a dark place, but more certainly, the stimulating effect of five or six bright yellow or red gapes flashing simultaneously in the nest, as the young open their beaks and beg for food, must exert a considerable driving force on the adult birds. As the young get older, this " gape-stimulus " is augmented by a " movement-stimulus " and a " cry-stimulus." Thus the young birds will reach upwards with wide open beaks

FIG. 9.—*Bearded tit nestlings showing the remarkable palate-markings. Note also the well-fed fledgling crouched below the others.*

as soon as they hear the parent bird approaching, and will move their heads and necks with definite movements which vary from species to species. Some young birds rhythmically sway their heads from side to side; others reach up and down with a snatching kind of action; others rotate their heads first one way and then the other. These specific movements have been very little studied and merit a careful and organised investigation. The food-begging cries used by the young birds vary too, from the plaintive cheepings and wheezy cries of the smaller song birds, to the sonorous purring of young owls. A very interesting case which will illustrate these several points is afforded by the young cuckoo. It possesses a huge gape with bright yellow edges and in addition the inside of its mouth is a brilliant orange colour. When in the nest it continually reaches upwards with wide open bill, whilst its note at this time is a querulous and continuous wheezy call. The combined effect of these on the adult birds acting as fosterers is very great. They busy themselves in a frenzy of effort to keep the young cuckoo supplied with food. In addition it has been suggested that as it journeys south on migration, the young cuckoo induces adult birds other than its immediate fosterers to feed it, by using begging actions, but this observation requires confirmation.

The lack of purposeful and intelligent behaviour which we have already noted in birds extends to their feeding of the young. They can be induced to place food into anything which resembles a wide-open beak, and this instinctive action has been cleverly utilised by some Soviet ornithologists in order to study the type of food brought to the young. Thus from a nest built inside a nesting-box, the young are removed and distributed among nests of the same species nearby. An "artificial" nestling is then substituted, and the whole so arranged that when the adult bird alights on the perch outside the hole, it closes an electric-circuit which operates the beak of the artificial nestling and causes it to open wide. The adult bird, seeing the wide gape before it, promptly places the food it has brought into the artificial beak, and this then slides the food into a tube below containing preservative (See Fig. 10). In this way, an accurate and scientific study of the identity of

FIG. 10.—*Soviet model for determining types of food fed to nestlings.*

the various grubs, insects, spiders and so forth brought as food for the young of one particular species, can be made, and provided adequate care is taken, there seems no reason why the method should not be developed and have a wide application. At present, the identity of food fed to the young of most insectivorous species is only known on the broadest of bases. That the placing of food in an open beak is merely an instinctive response to the visual pattern of the open gape itself, is shown by watching the manner in which the adult birds deal with the chicks when they return to feed them. As the adult, its bill stuffed with food, alights on the edge of the nest, the young shoot up their heads, with open beaks and clamouring cries. It will be noticed that the young bird which is most active in these "food-begging" actions receives the lion's share, and that there is rarely any obvious apportioning of the food evenly amongst the young. If one of them lies in the bottom of the nest and does not join in the general struggle, it is ignored. Now this apparent favouring of the chick that shouts the loudest is a direct result of the instinctive nature of the feeding reaction, but it does not lead to confusion nor in the long run to an unequal distribution of food, for as soon as one chick has fed to repletion, his begging actions tend to diminish in intensity, and his place as most active begger is taken by another of the brood. This one in its turn receives the greatest share of the next lot of food until he sinks back for a time, and another takes his place. This can be seen in Fig. 9 where five of the brood of bearded tits are clamouring for food, but the replete one, with a well-fed expression, can just be seen resting below the other chicks. So each chick in turn is automatically fed to repletion by a system which is totally without an intelligent or organised basis, but which none the less efficiently reaches an essential goal.

As soon as feeding of the young has commenced, there arises the further necessity of keeping the nest free from contamination by the excrement of the young birds. This is especially necessary during the first few days, when the young of nidicolous birds are so helpless that they are quite unable to do other than defecate into the cup of the nest. Unless the excrement were removed by the adult birds, it would constitute a real threat to the successful survival of the brood, and so we find developed in the parent birds a very strong instinctive urge to keep the cup of the nest clean and free from contamination by systematic removal of the faeces. This " nest-sanitation " as it is called, has recently received considerable attention, and we now know that there are probably two distinct phases of the process in most birds. In the first, the faeces of the young are taken as they emerge direct from the cloaca, and usually swallowed by the parent bird. After the first few days, however, the young, growing rapidly, are able to deposit the faecal sacs on the rim of the nest, or in some favoured spot adjoining, and then the parent birds pick them up after feeding the young and fly away to drop them at a distance. In order that such

" handling " of the faeces may be effective, the excrement is encased in a skin-like membrane, and so it can be picked up in the bill cleanly and removed neatly. There is a fairly set ritual connected with nest sanitation which most passerine birds follow. After feeding the young, the adult bird stands on the side of the nest in a tense and watchful attitude, and studies the young birds carefully. If nothing happens, the parent bird begins to fidget about amongst the young, pecking one or several of them gently on the bare area around the cloacal opening, or more often, taking a piece of the surrounding down in its beak and giving a short tug. This is the method used to stimulate the young bird to defecate, and usually has the desired effect. One of the young then raises its hindquarters towards the parent bird, and as the faecal sac emerges, the parent takes it in its bill and either swallows it or carries it away from the area of the nest. All the indications are that the removal of the faecal sac is an entirely instinctive action of the part of the adult birds. That this is so is shown by the following observations. A yellow wagtail's nest was found under a clod on a piece of fallow ploughed land, which had been heavily limed. It contained three eggs which proved to be the full clutch, and these hatched on June 3rd. A hide was erected and watching and photography commenced on June 8th ; when the young were 5 days old. The nest was in a deepish cavity beneath the clod, with a small tunnel-shaped approach down which the adult birds walked to the nest. At first the method of excrement removal was normal, both birds standing on the side of the nest after feeding the young, and stimulating them with occasional " prodding." The encapsuled faeces were taken from the cloaca as they emerged, carried away in the bill, and dropped at a distance. After about an hour, the lighting on the nest from a photographic point of view became so difficult that it was necessary to open up the nest-site considerably, and during this process, a number of the small balls of caked white lime with which the field had been treated, fell into the vicinity of the nest. The cock wagtail was the first to return and he immediately walked up to the nest and fed the young and then, without waiting for them to defecate, he seized one of the lime balls and walked

away with it. This was repeated many times, the area round the nest being finally cleared of these white pieces. The main interest in this observation lies in the fact that many pieces of caked lime had been in the close vicinity of the nest before the site was opened up, yet up till then had been totally disregarded. The reason for this appeared to be that the opening up of the nest-site had enabled the approaching bird to see the nest and the young clearly from a greater distance ; it had so to speak, enlarged the " sphere of influence " of the nest and young, and this additional stimulus had so acted on the cock bird that he instinctively picked up any white objects which lay near the nest. He also removed some screwed-up balls of white paper placed near the nest. When the nest-site was covered up again, the bird took no notice of the artificial white objects, but returned to the removal of the normal faeces. The area cleared round the nest was a circle about one foot in radius, and beyond this the stimulus appeared to die off. It seems clear, therefore, that in this instance, the action of the bird was clearly an instinctive one, stimulated by seeing the young and/or the nest. Which of these two factors was the dominant one was investigated in a series of experiments at a meadow-pipit's nest. When the young were two days old, defecation commenced, and the faeces were removed by both adult birds direct from the cloaca and carried away to be dropped at a distance. Later, during the fourth day after the hatch, the young were strong enough to deposit their faeces on a flat area at the back of the nest, which is commonly found associated with meadow-pipits' nests, and serves as a " latrine." Stimulation of the young by the adult birds was, as is usual, by prodding, and by tugging at the down and the deposited faecal sacs were carried away by the parent birds after feeding the young. Fig. 11 shows (top) one of the adult pipits stimulating the young ; (middle) a faecal sac deposited on the " latrine " ; and (bottom) the removal of the sac by the adult bird. When the young were six days old, experiments were commenced using artificial faeces made from white plasticine moulded to the shape and size of a faecal sac. The adult birds readily removed any of these that were placed on the latrine, but *they never did so if one of the young commenced to*

FIG. 11.—MEADOW-PIPIT AND NEST SANITATION.

(Top) *Parent stimulating nestling five days old.* (Centre) *A faecal sac deposited on latrine by nestling.* (Bottom) *Parent removing the faecal sac.*

*make any of the movements associated with defecation* ; movements which involve a shuffling backwards towards the rim of the nest, with raising of the cloaca. Under these circumstances, the faeces in the latrine were ignored by the adults, who " froze," tense and rigid, as soon as the young commenced the typical movements. If the young did not attempt these movements, however, the adult bird removed the faeces from the latrine. Prodding and tugging stimulation only took place when the latrine was empty. If the young were removed from the nest, the adult birds, on returning with food, behaved in a bewildered manner and ignored the faeces in the latrine, but the replacing of a single young one in the nest was sufficient to restore the urge, and removal recommenced. Hence the visual stimulus for nest-sanitation appears to be associated primarily with the highly specific movements of the young when they prepare to defecate, and the nest-site, together with the latrine and faeces, have no power as a visual unit to invoke the response which we call nest-sanitation. The young bird and its movements makes up the unit. Usually the feeding of the young is accomplished before the faeces are removed, but once a cock willow-warbler, returning with food to a nest with young, dislodged a faecal sac from the rim of the nest where it had been deposited by a nestling during his absence. After hesitating a moment, the male bird swallowed the food he had brought, and bore off the faecal sac. This points to the instinct to remove faeces being of at least the same order of strength as that to feed the young.

In stimulating the young to defecate, prodding of the cloacal area and tugging of the nestling's down is commonplace, but other forms of stimulation are by no means rare, especially if the nestling is slow in responding. Thus a hen reed-bunting became very " worked-up " with one of her brood which did not defecate after she had fed it. On this occasion she tried, on this nestling, first prodding of the cloacal region ; then tugging of down on the back ; then passing her bill right down the youngster's wing with a stroking motion, and finally seizing the young bird's head in her beak, she shook it violently to and fro. This produced the desired effect. The strength of the instinct to stimulate the young seems variable, but it appears to be stronger during the first half of the fledging period than the last, when the young have grown big enough to engage in active co-operation by depositing the faeces in set places round the nest.

To show how the instinctive nature of nest-sanitation can demonstrate how little reason enters into the actions of birds, we may quote the case of the pair of yellow wagtails at the nest to which reference has already been made. It so happened that on one occasion, both the cock and hen wagtail arrived simultaneously with food, and perched on opposite sides of the nest. Both fed the young and did a little stimulating. One of the young then commenced the pre-defecation movements and both adults became tense at once and waited. The young one raised its cloaca towards the cock and he proceeded to take the faecal sac as it emerged. The effect on the hen bird was immediate ; it was as though a coiled spring had been released. She flew violently at the cock, showing all the actions associated with threat display, and attempted to seize the faecal sac from his beak. Few actions could have been more strikingly illustrative of the instinctive nature of nest-sanitation.

During the period in which the eggs are in the nest, but more especially after the young birds have been hatched, the parents display a great many fear-reactions if the safety of their eggs or brood is in any way threatened. These fear-reactions vary greatly from species to species, and often from bird to bird of the same species, but are usually more strongly accentuated when associated with the safety of the young, than when the eggs are threatened. Many birds, when put suddenly off their eggs by a human intruder will scurry away with flopping wings and fanned, dragging tail. Thus the hen reed-bunting often sits tightly until put from the nest by a light touch with a stick ; she then jumps off the nest and flutters over the herbage for a few yards with wings moving in jerky spasmodic beats, before she finally flies away. Sandpipers, similarly disturbed, run away with feathers puffed out, head lowered and wings dragging, sometimes to the accompaniment of squeals very like those of a trapped rat. Some birds, on the other hand, fly to a nearby vantage point, and merely betray their anxiety by a soft call-note, like the plaintive " hew-ee " of the willow-warbler or redstart. Others again will fly right away and not return to the area of their nest until the intruder has left. Accentuation of the fear-reaction when the young have hatched gives an even greater variety of emotional displays on the part of the parent birds, and gives rise, amongst other, to the " broken-wing trick." This is well known, and manifests itself in the parent bird by an agitated and spasmodic fluttering around, with one or both wings dragging as though broken ; this action continuing as long as the intruder is near the chicks. These actions are very convincing to the uninitiated, and there are many persons, and not a few dogs, that have been deceived by them and have dashed after the displaying bird. When the danger to the brood diminishes, however, as the intruder is taken farther and farther away in his pursuit of the parent bird, and fear-reaction correspondingly diminishes and the adult bird finally takes wing and flies away. An interesting point is that if the intruder then returns to the place where the chicks still lie, the adult bird, although it may be watching from a distance, *never returns and repeats the " trick.*" It seems fairly certain therefore that the " broken-wing trick " is no intelligent or purposeful action specifically designed to lead the source of danger away from the eggs or young, but is merely the result of a real conflict between the instinct of self-preservation and that of egg- or brood-preservation. The degree of the fear-reaction produced is much greater if the intruder comes *suddenly* upon the bird and young. If the adult bird has had due warning of the approach of danger, it leaves the immediate vicinity of the nest and then the stimulus of the brood is correspondingly less and the emotional conflict diminished. Under these circumstances, the fear-reaction is less violent and may, in some cases, be quite absent. A most interesting psychological adaption is shown by the reaction of birds to various forms of danger. " Unnatural " danger, in the form of human beings, usually produces the maximum reaction under the best conditions, but the reaction towards natural forms of danger, e.g. hawks, magpies, jays, rats, mice, and so on, varies greatly. This is well illustrated in Fig. 12, where a hen reed-bunting is shown attacking a brown rat which was robbing the nest of its eggs. The attitude of the bird shows the fluffed feathers of the threat display, and is totally different from the fear-reaction already described above. Small birds will similarly attack other birds, like magpies and jays which, although capable of taking eggs and small young, are not usually dangerous to the grown bird. With hawks and falcons, however, the danger is greater since these latter use fully grown birds as well as young, as prey, and we then find that the reaction often becomes a true fear-reaction. Thus, in the case of an American wood-duck attacked whilst with her brood by a red-shouldered hawk, the young scattered whilst the duck feigned injury in front of the hawk, skilfully avoiding attack whilst maintaining an attitude of helplessness.

A very interesting problem, and one to which little attention has yet been given by field-ornithologists, is the determination of the exact moment when the instinct of fear becomes part of the young bird's consciousness. With nidicolous birds this transition point can be readily obtained by regular visits to the nest from the time that the young are hatched. The observer will find that for the first few days after the hatch, all the young in the nest will rise with open beaks and the usual food-clamour cries when he holds his fingers above the nest and makes an appropriate clicking noise with his tongue. Quite suddenly, however, on a certain day which seems to vary with different species, the young no longer respond to the artificial stimulus ; instead they cower in the nest, and in extreme cases will even feign death, with closed eyes and outstretched necks. Fear has entered suddenly into their conscious world. So far, we do not know how, at this critical period in their lives, the young suddenly become danger-conscious, and the study of this point alone offers considerable scope to the bird-watcher. Thus in young tree-sparrows, fear is acquired quite suddenly between seven and a half, and eight days after the hatch. With the young cuckoo, it is often sixteen days before the sense of fear develops, and the food-begging attitudes then changes to a snap at the fingers with the beak, or to threat display, with puffed throat-feathers. Young yellow wagtails change at about seven days after birth. It has been suggested that there is considerable survival value in the fact that the fear-instinct in nidicolous birds is thus kept dormant, since it seems to develop at the stage at which physical independence in the young becomes a possibility. Certainly the young of many species, especially those that nest in thick herbage such as whitethroats, hedge-sparrows, the warblers, and buntings, will promptly leave the nest several days before the normal time if they are disturbed, and particularly if they are handled. Young whitethroats ten days old will dive over the edge of the nest into the nettles and undergrowth if the latter are carelessly parted to view the nest. Such facts make it important that when the student of birds is recording fledging periods, he should be careful how he inspects the nest, and on no account handle the young when doing so. Otherwise recorded fledging periods may be in error by several days.

The position of the nidifugous birds is very different from that of the nidicolous birds just described. Here, the young are born with complete down-patterns, have sight, and can run as soon as they are dry after the hatch. The waders and game birds all produce such young, and with them the instinct of fear is apparent almost from the moment of birth. Within an hour, the chicks will respond to calls from the adult birds and immediately crouch motionless on the ground, with necks outstretched and often with eyes closed. Such actions would have little point if the chicks could be readily distinguished in their crouched positions on the ground, but we find that all such young birds are furnished with down-patterns which are arranged and disrupted in such a way that they represent some of the most perfect camouflage to be found. Young oyster-catchers and ringed plover, for example, practically disappear from sight when they crouch on the shingly ground on which these birds nest, and are then only found with the utmost difficulty. This protective coloration extends not only to young birds in down, but also to adult birds, where it is used for concealment during incubation (game birds, nightjars, waders, etc.), and also to the eggs of many ground-nesting species which are laid in the open, in nests unconcealed by foliage. With young birds, the action of squatting on the ground when danger threatens is entirely instinctive, and bears no conscious relation to the background against which it is done. The birds do not *know* that they are harmonising with their background and, indeed, they will sometimes squat in an area which, far from lending concealment, tends rather to accentuate their presence. Thus a family of golden plovers was disturbed whilst crossing a flattened patch of cotton-grass on a wet moorland area. The adult birds flew up and shouted the danger-call at the young, who immediately squatted right among the white plumes of the grass, where they stood out plainly. But such circumstances are most rare under natural conditions, and generally speaking the concealment instinct coupled with protective coloration, has great survival value for the young of nidifugous birds.

# CHAPTER 5

## INHERITANCE AND IMITATION

WE HAVE NOW reached the stage when the broods of young birds, safely reared and fully fledged, have at last left the nest and are scattered about the surrounding herbage. What happens to the young from this time on, and what their relations are with the parent birds, depends largely on whether a second brood is to be reared. If a second brood is embarked upon, the hen bird often commences the construction of the second nest (unless she uses the same nest twice, which is rare), immediately the young from the first have left it, and in such cases, the further feeding of the first brood devolves upon the male, or possibly the young may be left to fend more or less for themselves. But if only one brood is reared, it is usual for the birds to keep together as a family party at least up to the time that the adult birds go into the summer moult, and sometimes right through to the autumn. The period immediately following the quitting of the nest is the one most fraught with danger for the young birds, but it is also the one in which they have to acquire the majority of those accomplishments which do not come under the rather vague term of " instinctive actions." Thus whilst the ability to build a nest is an entirely instinctive accomplishment—since every bird can build its own specialised nest without ever being shown how to do so—certain other actions such as pecking-up food and ability to sing the normal song of the species, are not invariably accomplishments with which the young are born, and which do not need to be acquired. A great deal of the " education " of the young proceeds from a very strong instinct in young birds to follow their parents, and imitate their actions. The " following-instinct " has recently been shown to be associated in a very remarkable manner with the first living or moving object with which the young bird has visual contact after the moment of hatching, especially if that object is capable of making sounds similar to those normally used by the parent birds at hatching time. This remarkable fact which has been called "imprinting" (because, it seems, a visual pattern of the first living object seen by the newly hatched chick is strongly and indelibly imprinted on its consciousness), has been demonstrated in the following way. The eggs of a grey-lag goose were taken and hatched out in an incubator. At the moment when they were about to hatch, the scientist who was carrying out the experiment stood in front of the eggs, and remained there until all the chicks were hatched, and were able to see clearly the objects in the world around them. During this time he moved about and imitated the noises normally used by the hen goose as the young hatch. He found that from that moment onwards the young goslings regarded him completely as their parent; they insisted on following him wherever he went, even so far as swimming in the river with him. Other adult geese, even those with broods, were completely ignored. This is no isolated case, for further experiments by others have demonstrated this remarkable facility on the part of young birds of indelibly registering the first being seen as the one to be regarded as parent, and hence to be associated with thereafter. Thus a South American bittern, bred in captivity in the Amsterdam Zoological gardens, adopted the man who was tending it as its natural parent, and for ever after so regarded him. Although this bittern, a male, grew up and actually mated naturally to a hen bittern, it would immediately leave the hen and come to the man, if he appeared, and even at times drive away the hen bird from its nest, and try to make the keeper assume her place upon it! Similarly, a Muscovy drake which was hatched out by a grey lag goose and reared by that goose, always attempted to copulate with grey lag geese and not with Muscovy ducks, even after it had been separated from the grey lags for a considerable time. Associated with this imprinted image in the young bird's consciousness, is the urge to follow the object associated with that image, and to imitate in numerous ways its actions. Thus young chicks, especially those of nidifugous birds, follow their parents about and imitate their actions such as pecking up food, bathing in dust (partridges), diving under water (diving ducks and grebes) and so on. It is probable, however, that young birds do not have the ability to discriminate instinctively between what is good to eat and what is not, but that they learn this by a process of trial and error. Just how much young birds learn by imitation, and how many of their actions are inherited, is not known for certain, and there have been many conflicting experimental results. But it seems that the ability to perform most of the actions essential to its existence are inherent in the bird's make up, and that the urges of following and imitating merely assist in developing and improving these instinctive actions.

The theory of " imprinting " has an interesting bearing on one of the problems associated with the cuckoo. It is now recognised that certain cuckoos are almost invariably associated with certain species of foster-parents, and that these fosterers are usually of the same species as that which originally raised the cuckoo in question. Thus a hen cuckoo raised in a meadow-pipit's nest will for preference lay her eggs for the rest of her life in the nests of that species, and is in all respects a " meadow-pipit cuckoo." Since, on the theory of imprinting, an indelible and irreversible attachment to the meadow pipit must be formed in a young cuckoo raised in a meadow pipit's nest, it is easy to see why this cuckoo will seek out the same species in subsequent seasons, and use their nests for its own eggs.

One of the most controversial questions about this phase in a young bird's life, is that dealing with the acquirement of song. Does a young bird sing the normal song of its species through a completely inherited faculty, or does it learn the song through hearing adult birds of its own species singing around it and by imitating their notes until the song is learned? Superficially one would imagine that for many song birds the answer would be known, if only from the aviculturists, who raise young song birds in cages and often under conditions involving the hatching of the eggs of one species by the hen bird of another. But once again conflicting evidence confronts the bird student, and there is a really amazing lack of sound experimental evidence on this point. What seems fairly certain is that in all birds there is an inherited but highly variable, predisposition to sing the set song of the species, and that whilst in certain species this predisposition is so strong that the young birds will sing the song, or at any rate a reasonable approach to it, without having to learn it, in others it is weak, and the song has to be acquired by imitation. With these latter birds, placing them with song-birds other than their own species results in a song which more or less approaches that of the birds they are imitating. As examples of the first type of bird, namely those with an inherited song-pattern which need not be externally acquired, we can cite the blackbird, chiff-chaff and grasshopper warbler. The song-thrush also tends to come into this category, though experiments have shown that its environment will at times modify its song. Other birds (and they seem to represent the majority of species), definitely have to learn much of their song from adults belonging to their own species, and into this category we can place the robin, whitethroat, tree- and meadow-pipit, greenfinch, linnet, chaffinch and skylark. If young male tree-pipits or meadow-pipits are removed from the nest and reared in isolation, they will sing a " song " not unlike the grasshopper warbler in the case of the tree-pipit, or the serin-finch in the case of the meadow-pipit. An untaught chaffinch sings an abbreviated song like that of the lesser whitethroat. A white-throat and a linnet reared together both developed similar songs, resembling a mixture of a robin's and a skylark's. Whilst one might suppose that the simpler songs would be those which were innate, and the more elaborate songs those which would have to be learnt, this is not generally so. Thus whilst the simple song of the chiff-chaff does not have to be learnt, neither does the much more elaborate one of the blackbird ; the rattle of the chaffinch is not inherited, but the lovely rich melody of the blackcap is for the most part innate. That the disposition, in many birds, is to sing the normal song of the species, is typified by a nightingale which, though at first singing the song of the foster species by which it was reared, none the less reverted to the true nightingale song next year when placed with members of its own species. In general call-notes, as distinct from true song, are innate, although in certain finches some or all have to be learned. So we see that the inheritance of even so fundamental and specialised a character as song is by no means equally strong throughout the world of birds, and there is no doubt that this high degree of variability will be proved to apply to other so-called inherited characteristics when these latter come to be fully investigated.

As soon as the cares of rearing a family begin to come to an end, there is frequently a tendency on the part of the cock birds to recommence the longer and more vigorous periods of singing which characterise the early part of the breeding phase, and which tend to diminish as soon as nesting is well under way. It is almost as though, the burden of rearing a family being over, the bird were rejoicing at its new-found liberty. This we know cannot be so, but it is probable that the energy formerly dissipated in the great task of feeding and caring for the young is now being used to tone up the bird's body once again, with a consequent new flow of hormones through the body. Whatever the cause, the revival of song just as the young are coming to maturity is obviously of great value in teaching song to the young of those species in which it is not an inherited faculty. The cock robin responds rapidly in this way as soon as family cares are ended, and it is a fact that one can forecast that a robin's young have left the nest, or often too, that a tragedy has overtaken its nestlings, by a sudden and vigorous resumption of singing by the cock bird. That such a revival of singing occurs in the robin may be seen by consulting Fig. 3 on page 40, where the temporary rise in volume of robin song during the end of May and beginning of June is clearly to be seen. This revival in most birds is temporary, and by the end of June or the beginning of July, the volume of song has waned almost to nothing, as the moult commences.

There follow about two months during which time bird song in general is at a minimum, and then slowly, as the exhaustion attending both the end of the breeding phase and the onset of the moult diminishes, the birds begin to regain their sense of well-being, accompanying the general toning-up of their bodies. Climatic conditions and their general environment at this period favour them, at any rate in these latitudes, for the days are warm, insect life is at its maximum intensity, and food conditions generally are likely to be excellent. During this period, the gradual return of the birds' bodies to good condition is shown by an interesting phenomenon known as "sub-song." Thus in August and September the willow-warbler will sing a softly whispered version of its normal song, perfect in every detail of cadence and tone, but unheard unless the bird is very close. The blackbird will do the same on occasions, and so will the chiff-chaff. Later in the season, the chiff-chaff will completely resume its full spring song and this may be heard up to its final departure in late September. By this time those other birds—(robin, starling, thrush)—which show an autumnal revival of song, will have resumed singing, for the reason, already pointed out, that male sex-hormone is being once more produced by their glands, and introduced into the blood stream. We know, at any rate for the robin and starling, that some of these singing birds are females, and this leads us to the question of how many of our migrant birds sing in their winter territories, and how many of them that do sing, are females. Once again, we find that answers to such questions cannot be given owing to lack of facts. The willow-warbler, chiff-chaff, nightingale, sedge-warbler and blackcap warbler all sing regularly in their winter quarters in Africa, and since the hen willow-warbler has been proved to sing the typical song on occasions, it is possible that in all those species which sing in their winter quarters, the hen birds do so too, just as the hen robins do which remain in this country during winter. Whether the robin analogy can be still further extended to cover the possession of a territory in the cases of our summer migrants in their winter quarters is not known, but it is an interesting point worthy of investigation. The parallel case of the continental robin, which is a winter immigrant to northern Britain, has received no attention. We do not know whether these robins, which come to us from Scandinavia and northern Continental Europe generally, occupy territories here, or even whether they sing here during the winter.

We pass on now from the consideration of how birds learn to sing their songs, to the general question of how far it is possible for a bird to bring any intelligent process to bear upon the solution of a specific problem. There are two ways in which a bird (or other animal) could solve a given problem. It could accomplish it by the process of " trial and error," that is, by trying lots of different ways until the correct one is finally hit upon ; or it could obtain a solution to the problem by methods showing a true appreciation of the situation, so that the desired end is attained by an intelligent grasping of ways and means. From what we have said so far about the extreme rarity of intelligent actions among birds, we should expect that " insight-learning " of the latter type would with them be practically non-existent. Yet we need to know a great deal more about the ability of birds to solve unusual problems, and especially about their manner of arriving at the solution, and here the bird-watcher can do much valuable work, and incidentally derive considerable amusement and pleasure, by setting birds simple problems and watching how they solve them. Let us take a simple example. Most persons who are interested in birds have a " bird-table " on which scraps of food are placed in winter. Many too, string nuts for the tits to feed on. An interesting series of simple experiments can be devised with such strings to test the ability of tits and other birds to solve problems connected with obtaining the food from difficult or unusual situations. The first simple test is that in which a small piece of fat or a few nuts are suspended by a long thread from a convenient perch. If the thread is kept thin enough, the tits will find difficulty in clinging on in their usual manner, and must then evolve a new method of obtaining the food. The observer will find that some of the birds will solve the problem by standing on the perch, bending over and pulling up the string in their beaks in successive loops, and *securing the loops by standing on them.* This latter action is the important one, since the mere pulling up of the string to bring the food nearer would not require much intelligent forethought. But the holding of the string by standing on the slack shows definite progress towards an intelligent solution of the problem. Not all birds show this ability. The tits, and especially the great tit, have it, and so occasionally, has the common house sparrow. But the starling never seems to learn how to do it, and the robin, supposedly one of our most " intelligent " birds, is completely baffled by the long string. Bird-fanciers often use cages for certain birds in which the food and water are kept in little trolleys which run up and down inclined planes on either side of the cage. The bird inside obtains the food or water by pulling the trolleys up by means of string or a small chain. Once again it is necessary for the bird to learn that it must stand on the slack in order to keep the trolley at the top. Siskins are adept at this trick, and so are goldfinches, and sometimes a greenfinch will learn it, but it seems quite beyond the capabilities of some other finches, e.g. the chaffinch. In addition individual birds of one species solve the problem, whilst others fail to do so. There are obviously some most interesting and fascinating experiments which can be devised to test wild birds for intelligent behaviour, but it is essential to follow each operation most carefully before coming to a conclusion as to the method whereby the bird solves the problem. For instance, does a tit make several attempts to pull up a string and fail to hold it, and then by a lucky chance happen to stand on a loop and so learn how to do the essential part of this operation, or does it stand on the loop first time, and so show true insight learning? Naturally, if birds are marked in some way by coloured rings it will help the observer to come to a better conclusion, since he can then follow the progress of individual birds towards the solution of a problem. It is left to the ingenuity of the bird watcher to devise simple apparatus for his tests. One observer arranged an empty match box vertically, cutting a window in the broad side of the box a little way from the bottom, and placing a piece of card diagonally from the bottom front to the top back across the empty tray. A nut placed in it was held just above the window by the diagonal card, and yet it could be seen by the bird, looking upwards through the opening. The nut could then only be obtained by pecking at the top of the tray and so opening the box a little—the nut then dropped out. A great tit after many attempts to get at the nut through the box, was lucky enough to try the top end of the tray. In doing so, he pushed the box open a little, and the nut dropped out. This single experience was quite sufficient to teach this great tit the method of obtaining nuts from this particular type of box, and he never failed again. Whether it is necessary for the birds to be able to *see* the food can be tested by using first a glass tube (e.g. a lamp glass) in which to suspend the food, and then substituting a cardboard one. In general, we can say that we do not yet know to what extent birds discover the ways and means of obtaining food merely by trial and error, and thereafter have a flair for immediately benefiting from their chance experience ; and how far they bring an intelligent process to bear on the subject. There is scope here for considerable research, such as can easily be carried out by the ordinary bird-watcher from the comfort of a chair at his dining-room window.

FIG. 12.—(Top) *A brown rat discovers a reed-bunting's nest and starts to eat the eggs.*
(Bottom) *The hen reed-bunting returns, seizes the rat by the nose, fluffs her feathers in a threat-display and forces the rat away.*

# CHAPTER 6

## AUTUMN FLIGHT

As THE YEAR swings round towards the autumn equinox, our migrant birds, the moult over, begin to evince a new restlessness. The climatic conditions of their environment are now in a state of change, which is not unlike that of early spring except in one important particular ; the days are now getting rapidly shorter, instead of longer. The same cold nip is apparent in the early morning air ; there is a tendency for wide alternations of heat and cold, and just as the greatest variations in temperature in spring (which occur in May and early June) correspond with maximum sexual activity among birds, so it seems possible that the wide fluctuations of autumn may affect the birds in an analogous, but reciprocal, manner, and induce the tendency to pack together in flocks, or to depart once more on the long journey back to the tropics. Before the main tide of summer migrants sweeps down and out of this country, there are several phenomena of a secondary character which are worth noticing. One is the phenomenon of "dispersal" which shows itself by the scattering of the birds of the year over the countryside. Some of these young birds may make journeys which are most puzzling, and go northwards, instead of south, in the first instance. Thus a young sandwich tern, ringed in Fife on June 29th, was found in Aberdeenshire, 65 miles to the north on July 1st. Before the end of July, a bird ringed in Cumberland had reached Perthshire, 155 miles northward, whilst a Norfolk bird reached Angus 285 miles northward. Other young sandwich terns went south, however, and the scatter, although it has a slight northerly bias, appears to be fairly general around the points of the compass. Another phenomenon of the pre-migration time of early summer is the tendency of certain birds to begin to pack into flocks for roosting at night. The wagtails show this habit to a surprising extent, and pied wagtails will even begin to roost together in large numbers as early as midsummer. Yellow wagtails will commence roosting in flocks in August and September prior to departure. These communal roosting flocks appear to be composed of both young of the year and adult birds, and we know comparatively little about the reason for, or significance of, this habit.

One of the most baffling problems of the flight of the autumn migrants is the unaccountably early departure of the swifts. No sooner have these birds completed their breeding cycle than the restless urge to be off and away becomes increasingly evident. At the end of July, they pack together in great black flocks and sweep across the sky at evening, screaming as they go. In a seeming frenzy of effort they dash round their church steeples, or mount in ever-heightening circles into the sky. Then, on an early August morning, following a night when, perhaps, the wind has swung to the north and the temperature abruptly dropped, we find but few left in the skies around us. Why the swifts should leave thus early, when as far as we can judge, insect life is plentiful, and likely to remain so, is an unsolved mystery. The swallows and the two martins will be with us a further two months, and may indeed, still have young in the nest. Is it a question of a highly specific food supply which fails at this period of the year, or is another and as yet uncomprehended, psychological factor at work? Again, we do not know. The answer may possibly be arrived at one day; in the meantime observations on the mode of departure of the swift and the conditions attending it are of great value. One observer recently carried out a census of the number of swifts to be seen in the sky over the town of Oxford during the evenings of the second week in August, by mounting to the top of a high building and taking a "snap" count of the greatest number that could be counted at one time on any one night. The numbers from August 8th to 11th were fairly constant at 11 to 14 birds. During this time the weather was fine and the wind westerly in direction. On the night of the 11th to 12th August, it changed to the north, and the sky became overcast for a while but was then clear again with the wind north-easterly, and on the 12th the number of swifts counted by this method dropped to 5. By August 16th only 3 birds could be counted as a maximum in one snap count. Observations on August 17th to 20th yielded no swifts at all, and so by then all but the stragglers had gone.

The metereological conditions associated with the mass departure of birds in the autumn have had a certain amount of study, but this has been far too limited. From data so far obtained, it appears that migration tends to be set in motion by conditions of high barometric pressure, together with a favourable wind. In spring this often means an increasing temperature, whilst in autumn, it equally may denote a northerly wind with falling temperature.

The riddle of how birds find their way to a desired spot on the earth's surface is never more mysterious than when we come to consider the migration of young birds. We have seen that the young of the year, especially if the adult birds rear more than one brood, tend to wander away from the nesting area and may go in any direction, even north. Finally, however, in the migrant species, they must turn south and make their way to the tropics, and this they will do without any apparent help other than the innate faculty of orientation already discussed in Chapter 1. This is especially true of the waders. The North American golden-plover has a very remarkable migration route, for from its breeding grounds in Northern Canada it crosses south-east to Labrador, and then from Nova Scotia southwards over a wide stretch of the Atlantic to the Bermudas and thence to South America. The return journey is an overland route by way of Central America and the Gulf of Mexico, and thence right through the United States to northern Canada. But the young of the year do not go south in their first autumn by the over-sea route but take the land route by which they and the adult birds will return in the spring. This is a remarkable divergence, and these young of the year thus make a 5000 miles journey unaided across country they have never traversed before. This is no isolated case, however, for the vast majority of young migrant birds similarly undertake their long journeys with nothing but their hereditary ability to aid them. Young cuckoos leave this country several weeks after the adult birds have gone south again, while with some species like the lapwing, or the gannet, the young may commence their migrations *before* the old birds.

We have referred already to the possibility that, whilst the general route of the migrant bird is followed through an innate sense of orientation, the detection of the actual goal aimed at is finally achieved through visual cues and not by instinct. This view receives support from the behaviour of birds in thick fog. The starlings which roost on London buildings in and around the City, usually feed during the day-time in the surrounding countryside of Middlesex, Essex and Surrey, and they " flight-in " at evening to roost on the ledges of the tall buildings. If, however, a London fog appears during the late afternoon, the birds fail completely to find their roosting places, and pass right over London and on into the Kent and Surrey countryside until they clear the fog belt. They cannot *instinctively* find the actual spot they seek without first being able to see it. A similar case is that of the homing pigeon which has the " sense of direction " but cannot find its loft without visual cues. Once, a balloon let up in a thick fog at the Royal Air Force Station at Farnborough, Hampshire, for metereological purposes, was hauled down only to reveal an exhausted carrier pigeon clinging to the rigging. The bird had been flying about for hours utterly unable to find its way down through the fog, which extended to a height of 1000 feet.

While many birds carry out their migratory journeys especially those involving a long " hop " over the sea, by night, other birds are typically day-migrants, and from these we can learn much about the manner in which the journey is taken, especially over land. The swallows and martins are day-migrants, and near the South Coast it is possible to see the considerable flocks of these birds drifting southwards towards the sea. The flocks are continually changing in shape and composition, so that a bird which one moment is in the van may the next be well to the rear of the flock. There is never any indication of a leader or leaders, but the flock seems to exist as a broad unit which none the less shows variability within itself. Its only constancy is the general trend southwards. In certain birds, however, mainly the

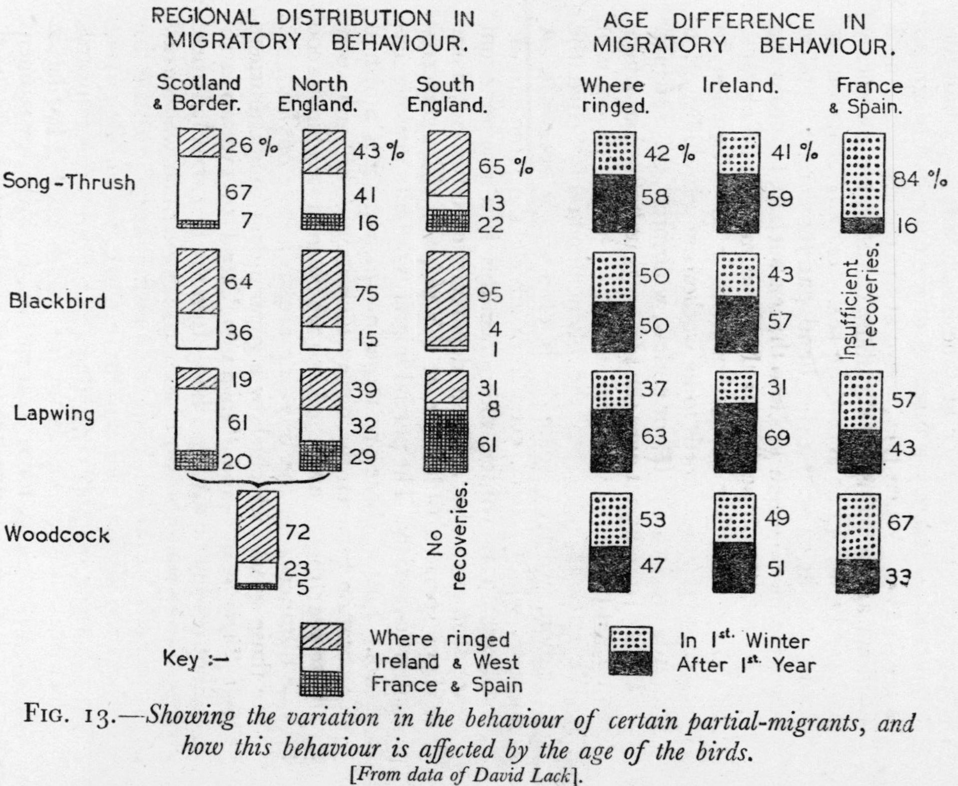


FIG. 13.—*Showing the variation in the behaviour of certain partial-migrants, and how this behaviour is affected by the age of the birds.*

[*From data of David Lack*].

geese and duck, migrating flocks do maintain a kind of order, and the skeins of geese, in perfect échélon formation, appear to have a leader at their head, although whether this is real, or merely a function of their method of flying, is not known. When they arrive at the coast, the flocks of swallows and martins usually show considerable confusion, and rarely strike out across the sea. They tend rather to turn along the coast, to either hand, and fly along until they find a peninsula which juts into the sea, such as, for example, Dungeness. These peninsulas then become "jumping-off" places for migrating birds, though their exact function in relation to migrants needs to be worked out more fully. Not all birds use such places, for curlew, whimbrel, and lapwings will strike straight out over the sea, without hesitation, when on migration.

We referred earlier to the phenomenon of "partial" migration, whereby some birds of a single species may migrate, whilst others, even from among the same brood, may remain to winter, and since this is a phenomenon associated with the autumn departure of birds, we may perhaps spend a little time at this point in discussing the matter more fully. The partial migrants fall into two distinct classes. Firstly, there are those in which there is a sharp demarcation between the birds which stay in the same spot all the year round, and the birds which migrate a considerable distance from the breeding area; and secondly there are those species which show a general drift southwards, so that "residents" and "migrants" tend to overlap and cannot readily be distinguished. Into the first class fall such birds as the song-thrush, blackbird, lapwing and woodcock, while many of the sea-birds, such as the black-headed gull, gannet and kittiwake fall into the second category. Recently, by collecting together the data obtained from the recovery of birds ringed as nestlings in the British Isles, it has been possible to decide, for several species, both the areas from which, and to whence, these partial migrants moved, and also the proportions of juvenile and adult birds which made the journeys. Some of the results are shown graphically in Fig. 13 where the breeding areas of the species are conveniently divided into three main areas called "Scotland

and the Border," "North England" (north of the Wash—Lleyn peninsular line), and "South England" (all England and Wales south of this line). The areas to which the migrant birds go from these three breeding areas together with the proportion of birds recovered in the reception areas, are shown on the block graphs by appropriate shading. On the right-hand side of the figure are shown the proportions of juvenile and adult birds recovered at the breeding area, and in the two main reception areas of Ireland, and France and Spain. Let us consider the case of the song-thrush, especially since this bird provided the most complete set of data for any passerine bird. Altogether, 174 of these birds which had been ringed all over Britain as nestlings, were recovered. Of this total, 74 were ringed in Scotland and the Borders, 37 in Northern England, and 63 in Southern England. Consideration of the graphs shows that, of those ringed in Scotland and the Borders, 26 per cent were recovered where they were bred, 67 per cent migrated to the west, mainly to Ireland, and 7 per cent went south to France and Spain. For the north of England, 43 per cent remained where they were ringed, 41 per cent went westwards to Ireland, and 16 per cent went south to France and Spain. Finally, for the south of England, the figures are 65 per cent resident, 13 per cent to Ireland, and 22 per cent to France and Spain. These figures show the following clear-cut tendencies:

(*a*) There is a sharp demarcation between "migrants" and "residents," for there are no recoveries, for example, of Scottish birds in South England.

(*b*) the migration is sharply divided into birds that go west (Ireland) and those that go south (France and Spain).

(*c*) A higher proportion of migrants from the north go west to Ireland than go south to France and Spain, and conversely, more migrants from southern England go south to France and Spain than go west to Ireland.

Turning now to the proportion of juvenile (that is, birds in their first year) to adult birds which stay put, or migrate to the different reception areas, we see that the proportions tend to be the same, and about equal, for the residents and those which go west to Ireland, but that of the birds which go south to France and Spain, 84 per cent are juveniles. This is a remarkable fact, and shows that there is a much greater tendency for juveniles to migrate south than for adult birds. On the other hand it is not clear why this does not extend also to the birds that go west to Ireland.

A similar general state of affairs exists for both the blackbird and lapwing, and although the returns are not so numerous for the blackbird, especially as far as France and Spain are concerned, the results are in general agreement with those for the song-thrush. The percentages for the lapwing are based on 509 recoveries and are correspondingly significant. The conclusions set out for the song-thrush fit these results excellently as well. The woodcock reveals itself as a bird which is highly resident, and there are returns only for the northern part of Britain. As far as the age of the recovered birds is concerned, however, the results confirm that the juveniles tend to migrate more to France and Spain than do the adults.

An interesting case (not shown graphically in the figure because of the small number of returns) is that of the robin. The results obtained demonstrate not only that the juvenile robins tend to migrate more than the adults, but also that, of the migrant adults, the majority are hen birds. This latter point has also been proved for the chaffinch and the blackbird among British birds, and for some American species. In this connection it is interesting to note that, with those species which are completely migratory, the females are said to winter farther to the south than the males.

If we try to arrive at the reasons lying behind the variable behaviour of the "partial migrant" species, we find ourselves in the realms of pure conjecture. It is possible that the autumn revival of sexual activity (probably due to male sex-hormone), which as we have seen, affects both male and female birds in some species, may give the breeding area a new significance and attraction in the autumn. This attraction is lacking in those birds, juvenile and female, which do not show the same revival, and which thus tend to migrate : The breeding area thus exerts a "holding action" on the stimulated birds and tends to turn them into residents. To explain the difference between the westward migration (Ireland) and the southwards one (France and Spain) it has been suggested that the former has originated comparatively recently from migrations set in motion by hard weather in the breeding areas, whilst the latter is the remnant of a dying, but old-established habit in which formerly all the members of the species were truly migratory. These suggestions are, however, mere theorising, for we have little or no evidence to support or refute them. The main difficulty is that the recovered birds are almost invariably picked up dead, so that we cannot tell what would have happened to them afterwards had they lived. It is possible that a bird which went to France as a juvenile might the next year remain to winter as a resident in its breeding area, or even go westwards to Ireland. Such slender evidence as we possess does not suggest that a bird of a " partial-migrant " species remains always true to its initial habit as either resident, or migrant to Ireland, or migrant to France and Spain. Once again it is probable that external conditions of environment, combined with internal conditions of physiological origin, decide how any one bird behaves in any particular year.

# CHAPTER 7

## WATCHING BIRDS IN WINTER

In the bird-watcher's year, there are two distinct periods which are marked more or less clearly by the two equinoxes. From March to September he is concerned mainly with the coming and going of the summer migrants and with the breeding phase of these and the resident birds. During the other six months of the year, from September to March, the winter migrants to this country occupy his attention, together with varied aspects of the behaviour of those resident species which remain to face our climate in winter. Not that any hard and fast divisions are possible, for a continuous overlapping of birds of many classes occurs, with winter visitors still with us in the spring, when the first summer migrants come in, and, at the other end, a great many summer migrants still here when the first of the winter birds appear in late summer. On the east coast of England it is possible to witness a considerable influx of birds, especially of the wader class, as early as the first two weeks of August, when some of the swallow and martins will have second or third broods of young still in the nest. Curlew, golden and green plover, and knot, dunlin and turnstone, as well as many others, arrive from overseas in considerable flocks, some of which may begin to appear in late July. This fact, of course, is well known, and many watchers have recorded the dates of arrival of such birds with meticulous care. But the far more important point, about whether these early migrants are adult birds, or young birds of the year, has not been carefully studied, yet it merits considerable attention. We know that in some species the adult birds leave the country in which they have nested, before the young birds which they have bred, and that these latter are left to find their way to the winter quarters unaided and alone. On the other hand, with some species the young tend to start their autumn migrations in advance of the adult birds, and many of the flocks of lapwings which cross the North Sea from the Continent in early August are composed entirely of birds of the year. Yet another variation is shown by the geese, which tend to keep together in family parties and migrate in flocks which are aggregates of several such parties. With the various species of duck, the drakes migrate first, as soon as they are fairly over the "eclipse" moult, and are followed later by the ducks and young birds. There is scope for careful study here, for provided the student can be certain of identifying the immature bird from the adults in winter plumage, he should be able to record the order of arrival of the birds, and thus work out to which category any one species belongs. Young lapwings can be readily distinguished from the adults, and it is fairly certain that with these birds most of the young migrate in advance of their parents. With knots, the reverse appears to be true, for adult birds still retaining much of the red which characterises their breeding plumage, may be seen on the East coast mud-flats in the first week of August, before any of the young put in an appearance.

We have seen that, in the spring, the whole tendency with the majority of birds (excepting the colony-nesters), is to divide and disperse over as wide a suitable area as is possible. As autumn comes round, we find the tendencies are mainly the reverse. Then, integration is the rule, and the bird flock or pack is the unit, rather than the individual bird. This again does not apply to all birds, as we have seen, for example, in the case of the robin, which is territorial and solitary in winter. Mostly, however, birds flock together for the winter, and we may well ask ourselves what advantages are to be gained from such flocking, compared with what would be gained by the same birds if they remained more or less solitary. One of the chief causes of gregariousness in birds is undoubtedly the fear instinct. They pack together for safety, and it seems fairly certain that birds in a mass *are* less likely to attack by predator birds than if they remained solitary. Thus the flocks of starlings which fly to roosts have been observed to have a distinct effect on any hawks which were nearby, the latter keeping their distance as the compact flocks swept by. If a straggler appeared, however, it was at once pounced upon. Besides safety from predators, the flock as a unit may in some circumstances be more efficient in foraging for food than individual birds would be, and here the more experienced birds will unconsciously help the less experienced. As far as the flock is concerned, it is as strong as its strongest, not weakest link, for the few birds outstanding in experience and ability will dictate, through their own actions, the main actions of the flock. Thus in flying in search of food, or in taking evasive action against danger, the birds with keenest sight, or swiftest reactions, lead the flock to sustenance or safety. The psychology and mental reactions of the flock as a unit are of considerable complexity, for there is often a " pull " between the desire to continue with the flock and the desire for individual action on the part of separate birds. This may be seen frequently with local bred starlings after they have packed together for the winter. When the flocks are on their way to the roosts and pass over houses and gardens, several birds will often detach themselves from the flock and fly down towards some chimney pot or house-top. Often they do not actually alight, but rise up again to rejoin the flock some distance farther on ; or they may alight and then join a following flock some minutes later. These birds are obviously passing over remembered landmarks or breeding places, and the pull of these for the individual birds may, in varying extent, help to destroy the autonomy of the flock as the dominating influence. Generally, however, the unity of movement and order existing in winter bird flocks is most striking, and the flocks of waders to be found along the winter coast-line afford striking and continuous proof of this. Watch a flock of the knots, dunlins, turnstones or redshanks resting, head to wind, on some sandy estuary. Suddenly they are disturbed by a passing longshoreman. As the man approaches, the flock, many members of which may have been apparently asleep with bills tucked in their scapular feathers, comes urgently to life, so rapidly that it seems as though an electric current has flashed through it. Each bird is, so to speak, on its toes, and as, finally, the man approaches to the danger limit, the flock rises as one bird and dashes out to sea. At first, as the birds fly low and swift over the water, we see only the dull brown of their backs. Then suddenly they turn ; there is a single synchronised flash of white as the gleaming undersides of the wings show for a moment ; then as suddenly and still completely in unison, a second turn restores the brown backs to our view. The rapidity of the movements coupled with what to our eyes appears as absolute synchronisation, is most striking and leads at once to conjecture on how such amazing unity of action is achieved. Many theories have been advanced. One has suggested a kind of instantaneous telepathy between the birds, in which the prior mental actions which govern the physical reactions of turning, rising or falling in flight, and so on, are communicated to all the birds in the flock at one and the same time. Such telepathic communication has been evoked to explain other bird behaviour, such as the ability birds have (and especially the birds of prey) of finding a new mate from a considerable distance away, when disaster has overtaken the old one. While at the present state of our knowedge, it is impossible to refute such suggestions completely, it is possible through careful watching, to look for simpler alternative explanations of such actions. Thus it will be noticed that most of the wader class of birds have remarkable feather-patterns or barrings which occur in their tails, and extended wings. These patternings, or at any rate, certain significant parts of them, only show when the wings are moved preparatory to flight, or, during flight, when the tail or wings are twisted to an angle as a turn or twist commences. In the light of this statement of fact, let us go back to our flock of waders resting on the sands. As danger approaches, we notice that one or two birds tense slightly, and the wings, the tips of which rest across the upper tail coverts, are brought slightly forward. Immediately a fleck of white, or black and white barring shows. This is a signal, and the electric current which seems to surge through the flock is nothing but an instantaneous reaction to this visual cue from one or two of the more alert birds. The rest follows in like order ; the apparently synchronised taking-flight, turns, soarings and fallings, of the flock are really the very rapid reactions of the birds to visual cues supplied by the feather-patternings of dominant members of the flock. The time-lag between visual receipt of the cue and the corresponding reaction is so small that the human eye is unable to separate the two, and hence we get the impression of absolute uniformity of action.

There are, of course, other birds than the waders which perform aerial evolutions in perfect unison, those of the starling flocks being noteworthy. In this case, the visual cues are not so obvious, but close study may yet be able to demonstrate that they are there. These starling evolutions are usually to be seen in the flocks as they gyrate above the roost preparatory to going down for the night, and when they are performed, as they sometimes are, by flocks of several thousand birds each, they make an imposing sight. The starling is, in general, a remarkable bird, and a close study by field naturalist and physiologist alike would be well repaid. We already know that the resident British starling differs from the continental birds which winter here, in having a revival of sexual activity in autumn, with consequent reappearance of song, yellow bill and other evidences of a sexual nature. Recently these physiological distinctions have even been advanced as a reason for separating the two races. Further, the habits of the starling in flocking in winter and flighting-in to communal roosts give opportunities for studying a great many aspects of bird-life such as speed of flight, course taken in relation to wind and contours, behaviour of the flock as a unit, and many aspects of bird psychology. Most starling roosts are situated in the plains, and there are few above the 600 ft. contour line. The birds may have a feeding radius of anything up to 30 miles from the roost, although 10 miles is an average figure, and the flocks have fairly constant flight-lines to and from roost and feeding grounds. It is of interest to consider a 24-hour cycle in the life of one of these flocks. Let us go to a roost before it is light on a winter morning, entering the wood quietly without disturbing the birds. We find most of the birds asleep, though there is a certain amount of subdued chattering and some fidgeting, by individual birds. As it slowly begins to get light, the birds show increasing signs of vocal activity, until finally the whole roost is chattering, whistling and chuckling. Suddenly, all the birds of one particular group cease calling and tense themselves. The transition from a noisy, relaxed mass of birds to a quiet alert one is remarkably rapid. Then with a sudden roar of wings, most of the birds in the group leap upwards and are gone. Sometimes a few of the birds are left behind, for with them, the impulse of the "flock-force" has not been sufficient to overcome the drag of the roost. These birds relax once more and may later join a nearby group and leave with them. The method of leaving the roost is always the same; the sudden hush after noisy whistling and calling, followed by the simultaneous leap upwards of the birds. By means of a photo-electric cell, it should be possible to determine what effect light has in governing the time of departure of the birds, and also the time of their return to the roost. It seems fairly certain that it is the *rate* at which the light is increasing, or decreasing, which determines the movements of the starlings from and to the roost; that it is not *absolute* light intensity is plain from the fact that on dull days, the midday light may be lower than it is at dawn on a fine day. We need, however, a good set of quantitative data on this point, and the investigations might also be extended to the movements of other gregarious birds, like rooks and jackdaws. During the day, the starlings feed in open country, on water meadows, pastures, or arable land, often in association with rooks or lapwings. They often consort too, with animals, so much so that an attempt to correlate the incidence of starlings with that of foot and mouth disease has been made. The flocks of feeding starlings number usually from twenty to thirty birds, and their eager, aggressive manner of feeding, with rearward birds of the flock continuously over-leaping the forward ones, is well known. As roosting time approaches, however, the flocks begin to fly up into nearby trees, where they sing and preen for a time, with other flocks coming in from the surrounding fields to join them. After a fair-sized flock has been formed, there comes a time when the same psychological state is reached as that just prior to the dawn departure. After much noisy whistling, there comes the sudden hush and then all the birds rise together and set off towards the roost. Other flocks join them, either on the wing or during short halts, which sometimes take place on the way, usually near the beginning of the flight. The lines of flight are often fairly direct towards the roost so long as wind conditions and contours allow, but the starling dislikes going over high ground, and where a hill is interposed between the roost and feeding ground, the flocks of birds tend to skirt round its base or follow valley routes until they gain open country again when they head towards the roost once again.

The roosting habits of birds have not received the attention they deserve, although we know details of some species. Sparrows choose the thick ivy on the walls of buildings, usually on the lee-side of the house from the prevailing wind. They also use holes in stacks and buildings, the main essential being that the site shall be dry and well-sheltered. A useful criterion of when birds become paired may often be obtained from observations at roosts, for in January or February, cock and hen birds may suddenly begin roosting together apart from the others, showing that pairing has probably taken place. Tree-creepers roost in cavities in the bark of trees like the Wellingtonia ; blue tits in shallow holes in trees, caused by the rotting away of a branch ; coal-tits on horizontal branches of cedars or in old nests in evergreens. Blackbirds use dense evergreens, especially holly, box, or ivy, and are very noisy on going to roost, keeping up an incessant " chink chink " note. Robins roost in thick yews and laurels, or in ivy, covering stumps of trees. The height usually chosen by these birds is 4 ft. to 8 ft. above ground. Wrens often roost in numbers, huddled together in a hole under eaves, or in a nesting box. As many as nine have been found together in an old song-thrush's nest, situated under the eaves of a low farm building. The method of roosting and the alertness of the birds during the night varies greatly from species to species. The blackbird is most difficult to approach at its roost without being awakened, but the nine wrens instanced above did not wake until a hand was placed into the middle of them. There seems to be a general relationship between the type of nest-site used by a bird, and the type of roost adopted. Thus hole-nesters like woodpeckers and some of the tits will tend to roost in crevices and holes ; thrushes, blackbirds, and some finches roost in evergreens, or low bushes like gorse; rooks roost in high trees. At the other end of the scale, ground nesting birds roost mainly on the ground. Partridges roost in parties, which often, but by no means always, form a rough circle on some fallow or stubble field with heads pointing outwards and tails towards the centre. Larks and pipits crouch in slight depressions in the ground, or under tufts of grass, while lapwings stand in small groups at random about a favoured field, usually facing the wind. Shore birds roost on the shore in positions which afford maximum scope for their protectively coloured plumage. Thus ringed plover and turnstone always resort to a favourite stretch of shingle for roosting, but dunlin and red-shank prefer a salt marsh or marram-covered sandhills. There are, of course, the inevitable exceptions to the general relationship stated above, and the pheasant, a ground nester, prefers to roost in trees, often at a considerable height, although the young roost amongst cover until about October, and adults will occasionally use heather or reed-beds.

In studying the bird flock, it is often instructive to determine the ratio of the sexes, if a sufficient plumage difference exists between the cocks and hens to make such separation possible. It was Gilbert White who first drew attention in this country to the fact that the main bulk of the winter flocks of chaffinches in the Selborne area were females, although Linnaeus had already remarked that the hen chaffinches of Sweden migrated to Southern Europe in winter, leaving the cocks behind. Cock and hen bramblings can readily be distinguished, yet how many have troubled to sex the flocks which seek the beech mast in their district each autumn? Some useful work has, however, recently been carried out, by counting the sexes of different species of duck which winter on the reservoirs around London. Great flocks of duck, in increasing numbers, have comparatively recently taken to spending the winter on the large reservoirs at Staines and Walthamstowe, and days spent on the banks with a good telescope have yielded some interesting data. Thus among the surface-feeding duck, like mallard and teal, the number of males was almost exactly equal to that of females, although there were slightly more drake teals than ducks. With the diving duck, however, the numbers of male birds were significantly higher than those of females. For counts of pochard, there were 72 per cent of males in December, and 58 per cent in February and March, with an average ratio of about 2 to 1 in males. For the tufted duck, from November to early March, the counts always yielded a figure greater than 72 per cent of males, although after about March 6th, the proportion of males dropped very suddenly. Comparative figures for the North and South of Britain suggest that the male duck winter farther south than the females, which is the opposite case to that of many migratory land birds. The saw-billed duck, goosander and smew, differ from the pochard and tufted duck, in that the females are preponderant. Thus in December and January, the proportion of males to females and immature birds in the goosander was 1 to 3, and in February and March 1 to 4. With the smew, male to female ratio was 1 to 1.6 in December and January, but 1 to 4 in February and March. Much more work along these lines could be attempted, not only for duck, but for many other birds too.

The subject of flocks of duck leads us to a consideration of birds as divers, for while some duck, such as mallard, teal, garganey, gadwall and wigeon are surface feeders, others such as pochard, tufted duck, goldeneye and scaup, habitually dive for their food. The length of time a diving duck spends under water is governed by several factors, the chief of which is the depth of water to be traversed before the bottom is reached. Others may be the nature and abundance of the food-organisms which are being sought at the bottom. One ornithologist spent many years in timing the duration of the dives of some twenty-three species of diving bird, making in all nearly six thousand observations. This timing was carefully done by means of a stop-watch, and whenever possible he measured or ascertained, the depth of the water in which the dives were made. From his results, he obtained a general " time-depth " relationship, which he called the " 20-10 seconds rule," which states that with one exception (the coot), British diving birds follow the rule that for the first fathom (equals 6 feet) of depth of water, 20 seconds is taken for each dive, and that for every fathom thereafter, a further 10 seconds is needed. This 20-10 seconds rule is approximately correct for all depths from three feet to twenty-one feet, the times for intermediate depths working out proportionately. Let us take a few examples. Some goldeneye duck were diving on a South Wales reservoir, where the average depth of water was about 9 feet. The average time spent by these birds under water during the 171 dives that were timed was 26 seconds. How does this fit in with the 20-10 seconds rule? By the rule, the first 20 seconds of the dive would account for 6 feet of depth, so that we have an extra 6 seconds left. The rule tells us that each 10 seconds after the first 20 seconds accounts for a further 6 feet, so that our remaining 6 seconds account for $\frac{6}{10} \times 6$ feet $=3.6$ feet (by proportionality). So that the total depth in which the birds were diving should, by the rule, be $6+3.6=9.6$ feet and we have already seen that it was of the order of 9 feet. Tufted duck, on another water, averaged 16.8 seconds in 4 feet of water, 17.3 seconds in 4½ feet, and 21.6 seconds in 6 feet. An interesting divergence from the rule is the coot which has a 10-10 seconds rule of its own, that is, 10 seconds for each fathom of 6 feet depth of water.

The same ornithologist has taken his observations further, and has been able to find the proportion of the total time under water which the diving bird takes in (*a*) descending to the bottom, (*b*) moving along the bottom in search of food, and (*c*) rising once more to the surface. When a bird dives, it usually ducks quickly under and then drives itself to the bottom by paddling hard with its webbed feet. In calm water, the propulsive force employed to take the bird to the bottom causes a column of water to be forced up to the surface, so that over the place where the duck has dived, an up-welling of water mixed with bubbles of air can be seen; a sort of turmoil on the surface. Because it takes some time for the disturbance under the water to come to the surface, this turmoil will last for some time *after* the bird has reached the bottom, but when it ceases, only bubbles of air (from the bird's "breathing-out") can be seen until the bird suddenly breaks surface on coming once more to the top. By careful analysis of his results, the observer was able to show that the total time during which the turmoil lasts is just twice the total time taken for the bird to reach the bottom. Hence if we time the duration of the turmoil and divide it by two, we get the time for the bird to reach the bottom. In order to come to the surface, a diving bird relies mainly on its buoyancy and does not force itself upwards with its feet, unless special conditions are present. This rate of floating to the surface can be calculated. It varies with different depths of water, and by using it, it is possible to give the average times spent by a diving duck in doing the three main actions set out above. An example can be given by illustration: In the case of the tufted duck already mentioned, 25 dives in 4 feet of water averaged 16.8 seconds. Turmoil lasted on an average 6.6 seconds, so that the time taken to reach the bottom was $\frac{6.6}{2}=3.3$ seconds. Experiments showed that a duck would come to the surface by buoyancy, in 4 feet of water in 3.4 seconds and so the total time spent by the tufted duck in searching for food on the bottom was $16.8-(3.4+3.3)$ seconds $=10.1$ seconds. It is obvious that some very interesting work can be done by timing the dives of water birds, and correlating the results with the depth of water, method of feeding on the bottom, and type of food taken by the birds.

A most interesting bird which is, in a way, a diving bird, is the dipper. The dipper finds much of its food on the bed of the fast-moving mountain streams and becks which are its normal habitat, and many observers have testified to its ability to walk about on the bed of the stream apparently without assistance from its wings or feet, which latter do not appear to grip the rocks and stones over which it walks, but are employed quite normally as on dry land. It will be noticed, however, that a dipper so walking under water faces the current by walking up-stream, and does so with its head lowered and back inclined upwards at an angle to face the current, and, in an interesting experiment, it has been shown that a flat piece of wood, pulled through the water of an ordinary household bath by means of a string yoke arranged so that it keeps the wood at a slight angle to the bottom of the bath, will stay down on the bottom and not float to the surface. The reason is that the force of the water on the tilted surface of the wood can be resolved into two components, one of which acts vertically downwards and keeps the wood down in spite of its buoyancy. A similar explanation may well account for what has been called " the puzzle of the dipper."

In concluding this chapter on birds in winter, we may perhaps refer to a method whereby the food of birds which flock together at this season can be studied. It is not generally realised that a great many birds throw up pellets of indigestible portions of their food, although those produced by owls are well known, and have already given valuable information about the types of prey of these birds. But other birds undoubtedly produce pellets, and if such birds roost in flocks, it should be possible to collect these from the roosting area and analyse their contents. This has recently been done for the curlew, which is remarkable in not only ejecting pellets of indigestible food, but also in periodically evacuating the lining of its gizzard by way of the bill. Analysis of the pellets month by month gave valuable information about the food of the common curlew. In July it was mostly weevils, beetles, with some frogs and in one case a small downy bird. In December, frogs, earthworms, earwigs and a few beetles were taken, whilst in February, one pellet consisted entirely of the remains of wood lice. Here then is a method of arriving at a wide knowledge of the food of many species, and since only recently has it been realised that a great many birds produce such food pellets, the study is in its infancy. Actual identification of the remains within the pellets is, of course, an expert's job, but the student of birds could readily arrange to have his specimens analysed through local museum officials. It will be realised that such pellets will only indicate certain types of food, and do not give the *complete* diet.

# Part Two

## CHAPTER 8

### THROUGH THE EYE OF A BIRD

In following the life of a bird through the cycle of a year, we have seen how visual patterns and stimuli tend to guide and direct its actions. A bird is evidently above most other creatures " eye-minded," and a thorough knowledge of how its eyes function and how they differ from our own, is of great use in interpreting many aspects of its life.

The first thing that strikes one on examining a bird's eye, is the relatively great size of the eyeball, and this fits in at once with what we have said about the " eye-mindedness " of birds as a group. Some birds' eyes are so large, and protrude into the interior of the skull so far, that the backs of the eyeballs roll on one another when the eyes are moved. There is thus little room for a large brain in the head of a bird. Only the smallest finches and warblers have eyes (6 to 8 millimetres in diameter) as small as the average reptiles, the group of animals to which birds are most closely related. Hawks and owls have eyes as big as humans, or even larger, which is quite remarkable when one considers the relative sizes of the heads. Birds' eyes can be grouped roughly into three classes, (1) Flat, (2) Globose, (3) Tubular. In Fig. 14 are shown as typical examples of these, in life-size cross-section, the eyes of a swan, an eagle, and an owl. As in the case of the human eye, the eye of a bird is divided into two main compartments bounded by the outer surface or *cornea*, the *crystalline lens*, and the rear inner surface known as the *retina*. The general functions of these main features of the eye are comparable with those of a camera ; the lens of the eye merely projects an image on to a sensitive recording screen. In the photographic process this is normally a plate or film coated with a chemical which is sensitive to light : in the vertebrate eye we find instead a membrane,

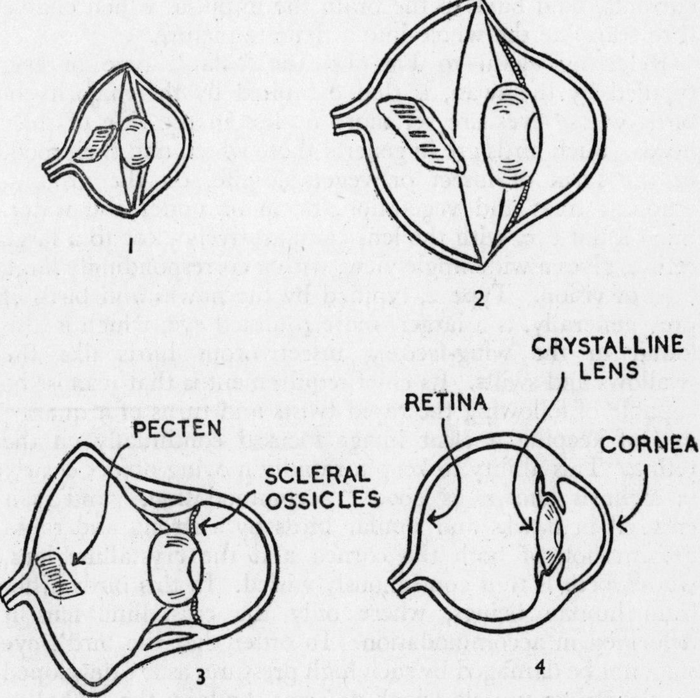


Fig. 14.—Different Types of Eyes (Shown Life-Size):

1 "*Flat*" *type as in the swan and many song birds.*
2 "*Globose*" *type as in eagles, hawks, and birds of prey.*
3 "*Tubular*" *type as in owls.*
4 *Human eye shown in comparison.*

the retina, which carries a large number of tiny cells which are light-sensitive, and which, by transforming the light focused on them by the lens of the eye into small electric currents, send back to the brain the impulses which enable it to translate the whole into a definite picture.

Referring again to Fig. 14, the "flat" type of eye, typified by the swan, is that exhibited by the majority of birds whose eyes are set more or less in the side of their heads. Such birds are in general those which find their food, in the form of insect or vegetable life, on the ground, amongst trees and vegetation, or in or under the water. Such a flat eye, with the lens comparatively close to a large retina, gives a wide-angle view, with a correspondingly large field of vision. Type 2, typified by the hawks and birds of prey generally, is a larger, more rounded eye, which is also found in the wing-feeding insectivorous birds like the swallows and swifts. Its chief requirement is that it must be capable of following the rapid twists and turns of a quarry, and of keeping a clear image focused continually on the retina. This ability to keep a rapidly moving object clearly in sight is known as good "accommodation," and it is ensured in hawks and similar birds by a strong and rapid deformation of both the cornea and the crystalline lens, whose focus is thus continuously varied. In this birds differ from human beings, where only the crystalline lens is deformed in accommodation. In order that the bird's eye shall not be damaged by such high pressures as are developed by the strong muscle which deforms the lens, the eyeball is protected by a ring of bony plates, known as the "scleral ossicles" which are very prominent in hawks and eagles. Finally, in type 3, the tubular type, we see the eye adapted to conditions of low light intensity. It is greatly enlarged, has a relatively enormous lens and iris, and is generally adapted to trap the utmost possible light. It is an eye found typically in owls, and also in their near relatives, the crepuscular or twilight-loving nightjars.

Let us now consider the kind of view that different birds get when they use their eyes in different ways (See Fig. 15 A). In the straight-headed forms, with eyes set in the side of the head (pigeons, song birds, etc.) the bird normally uses its two eyes independently, with both looking straight out sideways and registering two totally different fields of view. In this way a great stretch of ground on either side of the head can be scanned at once, which is obviously of great advantage in a bird searching for grubs, insects or small seeds. If it wishes, however, the same bird is able to bring both eyes to bear at one and the same time, on a single object directly in front of its head, and in this case both eyes, working together, register a single image as they do in human beings. When two eyes combine to send the impression of a single image to the brain, we have binocular vision. The field of binocular vision in such birds is, however, very small, and grain eating birds never have an angular field of binocular vision greater than 25° and many have less than 10°, although their total field of vision may be as wide as 340°. With hawks and birds of prey generally, and this applies also to birds which "fly-down" their prey like the swallows and swifts, the eyes are far less laterally set than in the case of the straight-headed birds. The heads of these types tend to be more rounded and the eyes set farther forward. This means that a much wider angle of binocular vision is possible, and it may be as great as 35° to 50° in some hawks. At the same time, sideways or lateral vision of the monocular type is still possible. The great advantage of binocular vision as distinct from monocular vision, is that it gives a single field of view in which the accurate judging of distances is possible. The hawk is thus able to fix his prey simultaneously with both eyes and to judge accurately the distances between himself and his prey before he dashes in for the kill.

At the other end of the scale from the song birds, we find the owls, which have eyes facing directly forward and have nothing but binocular vision. They have in fact, the most forward-facing eyes in the world of birds, with a binocular field of view of up to 90°. In addition, their eyes are so greatly enlarged, that they are jammed tightly in the socket, and cannot be moved as can our own eyes. To compensate for this lack of optical mobility, however, the owl is able to rotate its head round about to a remarkable degree, and can actually look completely backwards.

Certain specialised types of bird, such as snipes and wood-

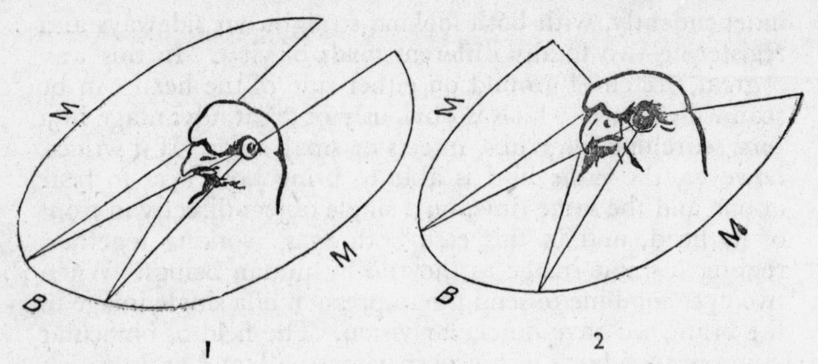


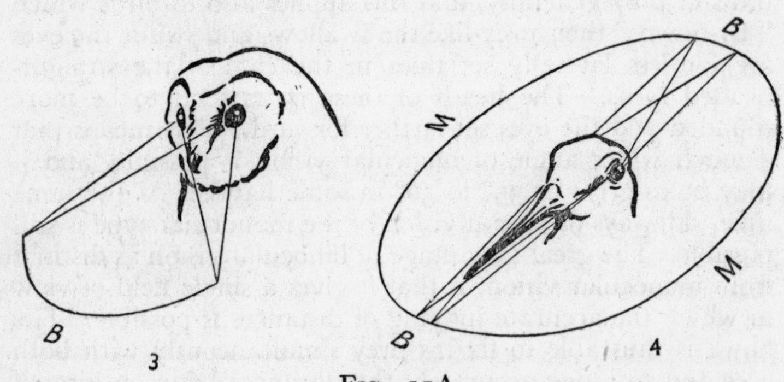


FIG. 15A

*B* = *binocular field of vision.*
*M* = *monocular field of vision.*
1 *Visual fields of a pigeon.*
2 *Visual fields of a hawk.*
3 *Visual field of an owl.*
4 *Visual fields of a woodcock.*

cock, have their eyes set very far back, so that the forward field of view may actually be less than that covered in the backwards direction. Such a system has definite survival value in these birds, however, for they feed by probing for worms with their long beaks thrust deep into the mud, and there is a real need for a wide back-facing field of view against possible danger. The bittern is another unusual case, for it has a curious "freezing" posture in which the bill is raised vertically upwards with outstretched neck, and the eyes swing forwards to focus binocularly immediately in front. The bittern thus keeps the point from which danger threatens accurately focused. (Fig. 15 B).

FIG. 15 B.—"*Freezing*" *posture of bittern, showing the eyes turned forwards to give binocular vision beneath the head, and towards the threatened danger.*

One remarkable feature of the eye of a bird is the "nictitating membrane" or third eyelid. The word nictitating means "winking," and this third eyelid is a skin-like membrane with a lining of tiny pimple-like cells. It is drawn rapidly across the eye-ball from the nasal side to the other and back again, and its function is to keep the surface of the eyeball clean and polished, and free from dust and dirt. There is also a marginal pleat on the outer surface of the nictitans which cleans the *under* surface of the eyelids, particularly in birds like the pigeon which usually close their eyelids as soon as the nictitans is totally across their eyes. In many birds (the owls and the dipper being notable exceptions) the nictitating membrane is quite transparent, and it has been suggested that, in flight, birds have the membrane habitually drawn across the eye so that it acts as do motor goggles in protecting the eyes against wind. Proof of this hypothesis is still necessary, however. It is of interest to note that in man, the nictitating membrane remains in an atrophied form as the "plica semilunaris" and this can be seen in a mirror as a crescent-shaped piece of skin lying behind the small fleshy "button" at the junction where the two eyelids meet near the nose.

We do not know a great deal about the use to which birds put the third eyelid, and bird watchers who use hides and are thus close enough to their subjects to see small details, could add greatly to our knowledge by noting the conditions under which the nictitans is employed. Great use is made of it by birds when incubating or brooding on the nest in windy weather, for their eyes seem to run tears in a high wind as ours do. Owls make use of their nictitans, which is a cloudy one, very frequently, and it has been suggested that they use it to cut down the amount of light entering their ultra-sensitive eyes during daytime. This again remains to be proved. (See Fig. 16).

We come now to a consideration of the most important part of a bird's eye, the retina, on to which an image of the object at which a bird is looking is brought to a focus. This membrane, which covers much of the inside of the back segment of the eye, is more elaborate in birds than in any of the vertebrates. It is about twice as thick as the human retina, and is remarkable in having two very sensitive spots or "foveae," compared with only one in the human eye. The need for two such spots is obvious when we remember that most birds use their eyes in two ways, namely monocularly, with eyes facing sideways, and binocularly, with eyes facing forwards. There must therefore be a sensitive area on the retina opposite the optic axis of the lens when the eye is looking sideways and this, since it lies near the central part of the retina, is known as the central fovea. In addition, when the eye is swung to look forwards as in binocular vision, the main axis of the optic system of the eye moves across the retina to its outer boundary or periphery, and we there find a second sensitive area, known as the temporal fovea. These two sensitive areas have been termed the "search" fovea and the "pursuit" fovea, since the first is employed in the sideways vision used when searching for prey and food, whilst the second is used in forward binocular vision after the prey has been located and the pursuit is on. Since owls have eyes which only face forwards, the need for two foveae no longer exists, and we find that the central, sideways-facing fovea has atrophied in these birds, leaving only the temporal fovea.

Many tales are told of the keenness of vision in birds, and it is of interest to consider whether anything in the structure of their eyes could lead us to suspect very high visual acuity. We have already mentioned that the recording mechanism of the animal retina consists normally of a large number of tiny light-sensitive cells, known from their shapes as *cones*, and *rods*. The cones are the cells whereby we distinguish colours, but they are operative only at relatively high light intensities. At very low light-intensities, only the rods can record. This accounts for the phenomenon that on bright starry nights we can see the shape of things quite clearly without being able to distinguish their colours. The retina of a diurnal bird (that is a bird which is normally abroad only in daylight), is composed of a mixture of cones and rods, but in the areas of the two foveae, the cones greatly predominate. With the night birds, such as the nocturnal owls and crepuscular nightjars, the need is for a retina with maximum light-recording properties, and since the rods are the cells which operate at low light intensities, we should expect the rods to predominate in such types of birds. This is exactly what happens, the retina of the owl's eye being composed almost entirely of rods, with few or no cones. We have then the two types of eye, the diurnal eye with cones predominating especially in the foveal, or sensitive spot, areas, and the nocturnal eye with an all-rod retina. We will now see how these two types of retinas operate to give maximum efficiency under the two conditions of day and night. Fig. 17 shows in greatly enlarged cross-section, the retinæ of a hawk and an owl. The hawk has the "daylight" eye, the owl, the "night" eye. The hawk's eye contains cones in large numbers and some rods, whilst the owl's eye contains only rods. Consider now how the hawk sees. If his sight is as has been suggested, much keener than ours, it means that his eye must be able to pick out, separately, a pair of distant objects which are so close together that the human eye sees them not as two, but as one. This ability to see a pair of objects which are very close together as two discrete or separate points, is known as " resolution " : the eye *resolves* them into two. If the eye is not sufficiently keen, however, resolution fails and only one object is recorded. It is quite easy to understand what are the essential features of an eye with good resolution by the following illustration. Suppose two bright points of light, very close together on a black background, are viewed from a distance. If the eye is to see these as two points of light, as they really are, it is essential that the images of the two points shall fall on two separate and distinct cells in the retina. If the images fall together on a single cell, that cell cannot record them as separate, since it will send but a single impression of brightness back to the brain instead of two impressions as required by the two points of light. Hence for fine resolution, an eye needs a retina with a great many cones each discrete in itself and each capable of sending back to the brain its own separate, distinct impression. In other words the retina must be packed with a large number of slender cells each with its own "private wire " back to the brain, for however slender the cells, if their nerve fibres ran together before reaching the brain, then the recorded image, although amplified, would be a single one. This is exactly what happens in the eye of a diurnal bird. We find the number of cone cells is greatly in excess of those in the human eye, and since they are packed into a small space, they are long and extremely slender. Each has its own single nerve fibre leading back to the brain, as a sort of " private wire." There are 220,000 of these cells per square millimetre in the eye of the white wagtail, whilst in the kestrel the number reaches the amazing figure of approximately 1,000,000 visual cells per square millimetre in the foveal region. This means that the visual acuity of the kestrel's eye is approximately eight times that of the human eye, whilst the wagtail has an eye about twice as keen. So we see that stories of the ability of birds to see far better than ourselves are readily explained by the known

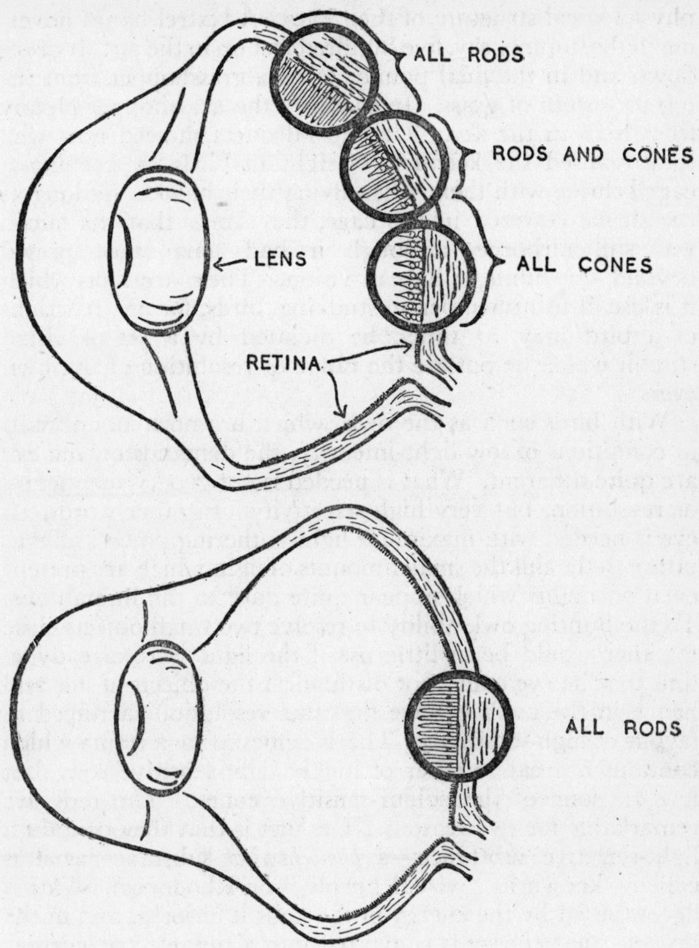


FIG. 17.—*The upper figure is the typical eye found in day birds. Note that cones predominate at the centre of the retina, with rods confined to the outer parts.*

*The lower figure shows the eye of night birds, with an all-rod retina, and few or no cones.*

physiological structure of their eyes. A kestrel hangs hovering in the summer sky, five hundred feet up in the air. It drops down and in the final pounce takes a grasshopper from the top of a stem of grass. It had seen the grasshopper clearly from high in the sky. The old falconers showed how well they realised the keenness of sight in birds by keeping a caged shrike with them when flying their hawks. So long as the shrike cowered in the cage, they knew that the falcon was still airborne, although it had long since passed beyond the limits of human vision. These are facts which it is useful to remember in studying birds, for the reactions of a bird may, at times, be dictated by a set of visual stimuli which lie outside the range or resolution of our own eyes.

With birds such as the owls, which are normally abroad in conditions of low light-intensity, the demands on the eye are quite different. What is needed is not good visual acuity or resolution, but very high sensitivity. In other words, an eye is needed with maximum light-gathering power, able to utilise to the full the small amounts of light which are present even on nights which appear quite dark to the human eye. To the hunting owl, ability to resolve two small objects close together would be of little use if the light were already so dim that its eye could not distinguish the objects at all, and hence in the owl's eye we find fine resolution sacrificed in favour of high sensitivity. This is achieved by a retina which contains a great number of highly light-sensitive rods, but few or none of the colour-sensitive cones. The rods are remarkable for two reasons. The first is that they contain a light-sensitive substance—a *photochemical* substance as it is called—known as "visual purple" or Rhodopsin. This is decomposed by the energy of the light it absorbs, and in the process, that energy is converted into a tiny electric current which sends an impulse through the rods to the brain. Secondly, the fibre cells which carry the impulses from the rods to the brain tend to run together as they pass backwards from the retina, and hence we get the phenomenon of "summation" whereby many of the rods combine to send a highly amplified impulse to the brain from a comparatively small amount of light energy. Added to this, the rods in the

retina of the owl's eye are very slender, so that a large number can be packed into a small area, as many as 56,000 per square millimetre being found in the retina of the tawny owl, so that the eye of the owl is one of ultra high sensitivity, and shows very definite adaptation for "seeing in the dark." Actually, the sensitivity of the owl's eye in conditions of low light intensity has been shown experimentally to be about ten times that of the human eye under similar conditions.

Since the eye of the diurnal bird is so keen, and contains so many cells in the retina, the demands on the blood stream by the eye are correspondingly increased, in other words, the metabolic rate is high in the area of the retina. In order to keep the retina amply supplied with blood, the eye of a bird is fitted with a queer structure known as the *pecten*, which projects inwards from the retina towards the crystalline lens. The pecten consists of a large number of small blood vessels arranged concertina fashion with their base resting on the place where the optic nerve joins the retina. It is thought that these blood vessels supply the added nourishment needed by the hard-worked eye of the bird. With nocturnal birds the pecten is much less developed, as one would expect in an eye with a correspondingly low metabolic rate.

It is of interest to consider what effect the predominance of the eye in a bird's head has had upon the development of its brain. Actually, we find that the large size of the eyes leaves little room for much else in the head, and so the brain of the bird is a small one. It is of the utmost importance to realise how this development of the sight-organ has affected the size of the bird's brain, for it interprets much of what we may learn from our study of birds. The scientific observer of birds who consistently refuses to allow his response to their actions to become an emotional one, will soon decide that in pure intelligence birds are on a lower plane than the higher mammals, although he will recognise that in intensity of living, and in the pitch and sensitivity of their reactions to emotional stimuli, they are on an altogether *higher* plain. Study of the bird's brain explains this, for besides its small size, we find the old primitive brain centres have been retained and there are no striking new structures as are found

FIG. 16.—*Showing the nictitating membrane in* (Top) *A hen ring ousel incubating in a high wind.* (Bottom) *A short-eared owl feeding young. In the former case the membrane completely covers the eye; in the latter it is shown travelling across.*

in the brains of the higher mammals. We expect therefore, and find, if we are honest with ourselves, that the bird is a creature almost entirely lacking in truly intelligent behaviour but abounding in what, for want of a better term, we call instinctive behaviour.

# CHAPTER 9

## COLOUR IN A BIRD'S WORLD

We have so far considered in some detail the structure of the bird's eye, and have shown how this structure has become adapted, during long evolutionary periods, to fulfil the requirements of sharp vision in the case of diurnal birds, and of maximum sensitivity to light in the case of nocturnal birds. But we know that our own eyes do more than pick out the shape and size of objects, or judge their distance away from us. Our eyes tell us also that different objects reflect the white light falling on them in different ways, and that consequently we recognise that they have colour. It is pertinent therefore to ask the question, " Do birds see colours as we do ? " We can seek an answer to the question in two ways, firstly by considering the physiological structure of the bird's eye to see if it contains the prerequisites of colour detection, and secondly by direct experimentation on the bird itself, by studying the reactions and choice of a bird when it is presented with a sequence of colours under controlled conditions. It can be stated at once that all the evidence points to diurnal birds possessing in varying degree, a fairly wide range of colour vision, but although the experimental technique of investigators into the fascinating problem of colour vision in animals has recently been greatly improved, it will be appreciated that the difficulties are extremely great. Several pitfalls have to be avoided, not the least of which is the assumption that because certain highly coloured parts of the bird's body have sexual, or survival value, that therefore the bird itself must of necessity, be able to see and appreciate those colours. This attitude arose soon after Darwin's theory of sexual selection had been propounded, when the habit grew up of assuming that since natural coloration generally had considerable utility from a sexual or protective point of view, that therefore those animals possessing such colours must of necessity also possess colour vision. There is a grave danger in all such deductions which spring from loose reasoning. Because we see a male bird using his wings, or crest, or breast feathers (all of which may be brilliantly coloured to our eyes), in order to display before a female, that is no sound reason for concluding that the hen bird can see and appreciate the colours as we do. It is possible that the shape, form, and brightness of the feathers, or the movement of the wings, may be a major factor quite apart from their colours. A completely colour-blind person can still pick out a great many objects of widely varying colours, because he distinguishes them on the basis of brightness, or in other words, the objects around him appear to be of a general shade of grey but differing greatly in their brightness. Hence lack of ability in a bird to discriminate between the difference in hue of objects in the world around it, would by no means completely neutralise the effectiveness of the use of coloured adornments in sexual display or as "protective coloration." Confirmation of this latter point is gained from the fact that it is usually just as difficult to pick out a protectively coloured insect or animal on an ordinary monochrome photograph as it is to distinguish it in the natural coloured group forming the subject of the photograph. With such safeguarding considerations in mind, however, let us consider the physiological and experimental evidence for colour vision in birds. As far as the eye itself is concerned, we have overwhelming proof that colour is detected by the cone cells of the retina, and not by the rods. We can say, therefore, that in those animals whose eyes possess a fair proportion of cone cells in the retina, there is strong presumptive evidence for colour vision of some sort. We have already seen that most diurnal birds have retinæ with both cones and rods, with an especially rich distribution of cones around the two sensitive "foveal" areas. But many of the cones of the bird's eye differ from those of our own in an important particular. Besides being long and slender, they also have contained within them small globules of a coloured oily substance. These globules are known as "oil-droplets" and they are a striking feature of the eyes of both birds and reptiles. There may be several colours within the eye of each species, and the range of colours, and especially the proportion of the different colours varies from species to species. In the diurnal birds, the oil-droplets are normally coloured red, yellow and orange, whilst in some cases, a very pale green oil has been isolated. What is the function of these oil-droplets? Early investigators thought that it was possible to find droplets of all the primary colours, red, yellow and blue, within the cones and on this they based their assumption of colour vision in birds. But they overlooked the fact that no such coloured droplets are present in the human eye, which probably has the most perfect colour vision amongst animals. That the coloured droplets must affect profoundly the colour-sensitivity of birds is certain, for they will act as coloured filters, in exactly the same way as do filters placed before a camera lens. It seems probable that their main function is to ensure that only certain regions of the visible spectrum get through to the base of the cones, so that the colour vision of any one particular species is to that extent limited, or rather specified. We shall return later to a consideration of the possibility of colour awareness being variable with different species, but it is clearly indicated that since the colour and distribution of oil-droplets varies from species to species, there is strong evidence for assuming that a bird of one species may be more sensitive to certain parts of the visible spectrum than another of a different species. Since the oil droplets are in the main coloured red or yellow, their filter effect will tend to restrict the amount of light from the blue end of the spectrum which reaches the sensitive limb of the cone, and thus reduce the amount of the more highly scattered light getting through. This would give improved visibility of distant objects in exactly the same way as an infra-red photographic plate enables objects to be photographed through mist. This filter-effect of the oil-droplets may have considerable survival value for many species. Thus, in the pigeon the lower three-quarters of the retina has yellow droplets predominating, whilst the upper quarter has excess of red droplets. Since the image on the retina is an inverted one, the image of the sky falls on the lower part of the retina of the pigeon, and the blue of the sky is so toned down by the yellow droplets, that the enhanced contrast resulting enables the pigeon to see objects against the blue of the sky much more easily. Hence danger in the form of a hawk is the more readily seen. At the same time, the green of the fields and trees over which the bird is flying is filtered by the red droplets to give maximum visibility.

As far as the oil-droplets are concerned, the song birds have about 20 per cent, the hawks about 10 per cent, and the swifts and swallow about 3 per cent to 5 per cent of their total droplets, red. The kingfisher is remarkable in having about 60 per cent of its retinal oil-droplets red, and it has been pointed out that this is probably associated with the special problem the kingfisher has of dealing with bright glare reflected from the surface of water. A red filter is certainly very effective in cutting this down. The general filter effect of the oil-droplets is thus to cut down the shorter wave-length of the blue end of the spectrum, and enhance vision at the longer wave-length of the red end. In the nocturnal birds such as the owls, we find an eye with practically a cone-free retina, the rods greatly predominating. Hence we anticipate that the colour sensitivity of these birds will be very small, and this is confirmed by experiment. It has been shown that owls are sensitive to blue light, but they do not respond at all to light at the red end of the spectrum. This of course is in keeping with the fact that the rods contain the purple-coloured, photochemical substance, rhodopsin, which does not absorb any light of the longer wave-lengths at the red end of the spectrum.

To sum up the physiological factors affecting colour vision in birds, we can say that the presence of cones in day-birds indicates colour vision, and that these cones, having incorporated within them tiny filters as coloured oil-droplets, probably give specific colour discrimination, and certainly specialised visual acuity, to different species of birds. With night-birds, absence of cones indicates absence of colour vision, in other words the vision of nocturnal birds is almost certainly achromatic.

We now turn to the experimental investigations into colour-awareness in birds. They have generally been of two kinds; the laboratory experiment under strictly controlled conditions with caged birds and the experiments in the field with wild birds. Of these two types, the former greatly predominate. As has been mentioned, the pitfalls in such investigations are numerous and often most difficult to detect. The technique usually adopted is to colour the food of the bird, either directly with dyes or by illuminating it with spectral colours, and then to study the preference shown by the bird in picking up the food. Such experiments have mostly been carried out on the domestic hen and the pigeon, and one has to be quite certain that the birds are not making their choice from a preference in the *position* of one particular colour, or from its brightness as distinct from its actual colour. The overlooking of such considerations led many early investigators astray, but the best of the later experiments have produced results about which there can be little or no doubt. The " positional preference " error is readily eliminated by making a significant number of experiments in which the positions of the different groups of coloured grain are continually varied, whilst the " brightness preference " is controlled by actual measurements of the amount of reflected light from each colour, so that different colours can be adjusted to have the same degree of brightness. By such methods it has been shown that the domestic hen can discriminate many colours and its ability in this respect is not very much less than that of man. The minimum intensity of any one colour which its eye could detect was similar to that of the human eye, except at the red end of the spectrum, where it was slightly better, and at the blue end, where its response to blue and violet was notably weaker than the human eye. The fowl also managed to pick out different colours from white of a similar brightness.

Hue discrimination in the pigeon, while it is less than in man, has been shown to cover a considerable range of the visible spectrum, and there is always the possibility to consider that apparent lack of fine discrimination of colour in the lower animals may be a reflection more of their lower intelligence than of actual failure on the part of their eyes to discern the colours.

In the case of the Australian zebra grass-parakeet, a little budgerigar known as the shell-parrot, extensive and careful investigations have shown that this bird possesses neither the comparative blue-blindness nor the extra sensitivity to red, exhibited by the domestic hen, but can discriminate blues and violets from greys about as readily as it can other colours. On the other hand, shades of grey were picked out only with difficulty. It is interesting to note again, that this budgerigar lacks the deep red oil-droplets present in the hen and pigeon, and the absence of such oil-droplets accounts for the fact that the blue discrimination of this bird is better than that of birds whose retinæ contain the red type of oil-droplet, since these latter tend to absorb and not to transmit light at the blue end of the spectrum.

Another laboratory method of testing the response of a bird to colours, is to make use of the fact that the pupil of an eye will contract when exposed to light to an extent which bears a direct relationship to the degree of retinal response. This is merely another way of saying that the brain automatically adjusts the amount of light reaching the retina, by operating the muscles which control the expansion or contraction of the iris. This is known as the Sach effect, and by using it, investigators in this field have been able to compare the visual responses of man with those of birds. Thus a totally colour-blind (" achromatic ") man was used in one series of trials in which two lights, one red, and the other blue, were adjusted in intensity until the pupils of the man's eyes remained unaltered in size when the two lights were alternately presented to them. The two lights were now of equal *brightness* for the achromatic man. These were now presented alternately to the eyes of both a pigeon and a little owl, when the pigeon was less affected by the blue than the red light, whilst the pupil of the owl contracted more for the blue than the red. Using this technique with various colours, it was possible to demonstrate that the eye of the pigeon was less sensitive to green and blue than the human eye, whilst the eyes of four species of owls were more sensitive to blue than the human eye. Laboratory experiments as far as they have gone, therefore lead us to the conclusion that diurnal birds have colour vision which differs from our own mainly in being less sensitive to blues and more sensitive to reds, whilst the nocturnal birds have little true colour vision, but have eyes which see blues as light shades of grey, and reds probably as dark greys or even blacks.

We turn now from the laboratory to the field. How do these facts fit in with the behaviour of the wild bird as it lives its natural life? The humming birds are interesting from this point of view, for they get their sustenance mainly from the honey and nectar of flowers, and what is more they greatly favour flowers which are red or "fire" coloured. Experiments have shown too, that the humming birds are initially attracted to flowers by their colours, since it is possible to deceive these birds with orange berries and even with carrots! The ruby-throated humming bird shows a very marked preference for red flowers, and it has been suggested that red flowers can be seen at a greater distance by these birds than flowers of other colours.

Other birds which provide us, in their natural state, with information about their colour-awareness, are the Australasian Bower birds. In this remarkable group, the male birds have the habit of constructing, in the breeding season, a "bower," which is quite independent of, and sometimes quite away from, the site of the nest. This bower is decorated with coloured objects such as flowers, feathers, berries, shells, stones, or bones, whilst some species plaster the inside of the bower with coloured fruit pulp, and macerated wood or charcoal. The Satin bower-bird has been especially studied from this point of view. It has been shown that the bowers and their decorations have little to do with sexual selection, but that their primary function is sexual stimulation by visual means. In the case of the satin bower-bird, selection of coloured decorations for the bower closely matches the colours of the female, especially the colours of those parts of her plumage which have sexual significance. Thus the cock satin bower-bird will choose blue, lemon-yellow, and grey-brown objects for decoration, and for a blue object, it will search assiduously for the tail feathers of the Australian parakeet. It has even been known to steal a blue-bag, and blue cigarette packets, whilst ignoring those coloured red! The correlation of the choice of colours with the more prominent colours of the plumage of the female opens up exciting possibilities in the study of colour vision among birds, for here we have a *natural* experiment conducted by the bird itself with no outside training or influence. Unfortunately the evidence for the other bower birds, so far as we know it, is somewhat contradictory. The spotted bower-bird, a speckled brown bird with a bright mauve-red neck-tuft, shows preference for green and white objects, the white objects often consisting of bleached bones. Sometimes, with this species, green berries which have been placed in the bower as decorations, turn red or yellow, and are then promptly rejected. Yet another species, Newton's bower-bird, with brown and yellow plumage, collects white flowers. Hence the correlation between choice of colours and plumage does not extend to all the bower-birds, but the study of these birds is in its infancy and they will obviously repay careful and detailed investigation. It would be especially interesting to know the colours and proportions of the oil-droplets within their retinæ. The main point, however, is that they lend strong natural evidence of the colour awareness of their group of birds.

Finally, we come to experiments carried out on birds in the field. These have not been numerous, and too often have been rendered useless by the fact that the colours referred to have not been scientifically designated. Thus experimenters have stained nuts, hung out for tits, with various colours and noted the order of preference with which the tits attacked the nuts. Others have supplied nest-building birds with materials variously coloured, and again noted the preference of choice. But almost all such experiments have been of little scientific use because the colours have been referred to by names like "red," "yellow," "blue," "green" and so on. By themselves such names mean little scientifically; what is needed is an absolute measure of the colour of the reflected light. Very few reflected colours are "pure," that is, most of them are composed of a mixture of many colours, the proportions of which control the main sensation of colour which reaches the eye. To analyse the mixture of colours which combine to make a given colour, requires specialised apparatus which is only to be found in well-equipped laboratories, but it is possible for the serious amateur to get quite a good designation for any set of colours he may wish to employ in experimenting with the colour awareness of birds, by the use of the Munsell book of colour. This book, which may be consulted at many of the larger libraries, has a number of colour-graphs, each colour being based on the three fundamental properties of *hue*, which is the actual *description* of the colour, such as red, yellow, green and so on; *value*, which is really a measure of the brightness of the colour and is matched against a series of grey standards; and *chroma* which is the measure of the strength of the colour, or its saturation or intensity. Any unknown colour can be matched against one of the colours given in the Munsell charts, and then adequately designated numerically in terms of hue, value and chroma.

In order to place a series of colours in the order of their brightness factor (or *value* in terms of the Munsell system), an alternative method is to employ a photo-electric exposure meter such as is used commonly in photography. This is quite accurate enough to place most coloured objects in order of their brightness as distinct from their colour or hue. In this way it is possible to give a colour some degree of scientific significance, and would-be experimenters in this field should make every effort to do this.

The instinct of nest sanitation whereby most birds, and especially the small song-birds, keep their nests free from the droppings of the young by carrying away the faecal sacs, has been employed in one series of field experiments, in order to test the colour-responses of the yellow wagtail and the meadow-pipit. Thus at nests of both these species which contained young, artificial faeces of different colours made from "Plasticine," moulded to the correct shape and size, were placed on the rim of the nest, and the order of removal by the parent birds was noted. The brightness of the reflected light, independent of its colour, and also the wave lengths of the colours themselves, were measured. Precautions were taken to change the arrangement of the colours on the nest-rim for each successive trial, so that any "positional preference" error was eliminated. The data giving the spectral measurements and also the brightness, of the colours used, is given in Table I.

TABLE I.

| Colour. | Brightness Factor. | Hue Wave-length $\mu\mu$. | Saturation. |
|---|---|---|---|
| White | 0.586 | 578 | 0.156 |
| Yellow | 0.362 | 578 | 0.448 |
| Green | 0.222 | 549 | 0.348 |
| Red | 0.134 | 492C | 0.228 |
| Purple | 0.116 | 566C | 0.006 |

(C=Complementary colour).

If the birds were colour blind, the order of removal would be in the order of decreasing brightness factor, but the trials showed no such preference for the brighter faeces (see Table II), but rather were they removed in a definite order which left no doubt that the colours themselves were governing the choice.

Table II shows the order of removal of the different coloured faeces by the two species of bird.

TABLE II.

| Species. | Trial. | Red. | Yellow. | Green. | Purple. | White |
|---|---|---|---|---|---|---|
| Meadow-Pipit. | *a* | 4 | 3 | 1 | Ignored | 2 |
| | *b* | 4 | 3 | 1 | 5 | 2 |
| | *c* | 5 | 3 | 2 | 4 | 1 |
| | *d* | 4 | 3 | 1 | Ignored | 2 |
| | *e* | 4 | 3 | 1 | 5 | 2 |
| Yellow Wagtail | *a* | 5 | 1 | 4 | 3 | 2 |
| | *b* | 5 | 1 | 4 | 3 | 2 |
| | *c* | 4 | 1 | 5 | 2 | 3 |
| | *d* | 5 | 2 | 4 | 1 | 3 |

Figure 18 A shows the female meadow-pipit removing, during trial c, the yellow (Y), while the red (R) and purple (P) faeces remain on the rim of the nest. Figure 18 B shows the male yellow wagtail removing, in trial (d), the yellow (Y), whilst white (W), green (G) and red (R) remain.

It is evident that, to the meadow-pipit, green must be a very significant colour, since in four out of five trials it was taken as first choice. Yellow occupies an intermediate position, and red and purple last choices, purple particularly failing to attract attention. With the yellow wagtail, on the other hand, the order of choice was strikingly different. With this pair of birds, the female refused all the artificial faeces except the white ones, but the male readily removed them all. His first choice was yellow in three out of four trials, after which he took purple or white. In trial *d*, purple was first choice. Green on the other hand, was the penultimate, and red the last choice, three times in four. These results are in striking contrast to those obtained with the meadow-pipit, especially in relation to the significance of yellow and purple. Pipits and wagtails both belong to the same family of birds (*Motacillidae*), but whilst the former tend to have dull brown and olive plumages, the wagtails are often brightly coloured, with yellow and blue frequently predominating. There is an indication here that there may be a correlation between the colour awareness of a bird and the plumage colours of the species, but by themselves the experiments are no more than an indication. What is needed is a great deal more work of this, and similar character, under carefully controlled conditions. We know very little about the proportions and type of the various oil-droplets in the cones of the avian retina, except in a few of the commoner species, and we know very little about the response of birds to colour in relation to their surroundings. We have limited indications that there may be a correlation between plumage colours and response to various colours ; we surmise that the oil-droplets may help this correlation by acting as specific inter-occular filters. This is the present position, and it is obvious that the surface is hardly scratched. It remains true that the only animal whose colour responses are known with any degree of certainty is man. In the study of birds from this point of view, a wide and intensely interesting field of investigation is open.

The colours to be found in the feathers of birds make an interesting study. They are of two kinds, namely, the colours arising from actual pigmentation of the feathers, and those arising from the splitting up of the incident white light at the fine feather structure. This latter is by far the more common of the two causes of colour in feathers, the number of colours given by pigments being remarkably small. The light is split up by minute air-bubbles which are trapped in the tiny barbules of the feather structure, the surface of the bubbles splitting up the incident light in exactly the same way as a thin film of oil on a puddle of water splits it into all the colours of the rainbow. Such colours are known as "structural colours" as distinct from "pigment colours." There is no blue pigment in the feathers of any bird, all blue in feathers arising from structural causes. No coloured pigments of any kind exist in the tail or breast feathers of the peacock. In the American blue jay, the flight feathers are blue with a prominent white tip. If the feathers are examined, it is found that the part appearing blue is backed internally by a *black* pigment, and if one dips the white tip into Indian ink, the tip immediately appears blue like the rest of the feather. The sheen and colours to be seen on the starling, magpie, rook and a host of other birds in certain lights, are all examples of structural colours, allied to the "metallic" colours of beetles. There are blue pigments to be found in flowers and the skins of some animals, and hence their absence in birds' feathers is surprising. Green colours in the feathers of birds may be due in some instances to a green pigment, but most green feathers owe their colour to the combined effect of a structural blue and a pigment yellow.

One group of birds with pigmented feathers are the African touracons, which are birds intermediate in appearance between a jay and a pheasant. They are forest birds, and have bright red feathers in the wings. A remarkable thing about this red colour is that it is a pigment colour which is soluble in mildly alkaline water, such as for example, a soap solution. The pigment, on analysis, has been shown to be a copper salt of the chemical " porphyrin," and a quill feather lighted at a flame will burn a bright green colour due to the copper in the pigment.

# CHAPTER 10

## A BIRD IN THE AIR

THE GREATEST single factor which separates birds from other vertebrate animals, and gives them their specific character, is their ability to fly. Apart from a few animals like the flying foxes, flying fish, and certain exotic frogs (which cannot be said truly to fly, but rather glide with the aid of specially developed membranes), birds and bats are the only existing vertebrates which have, by natural evolution, developed true organs of flight. Both have evolved from primitive lizards, the best flying member of which group was the pterodactyl, which had a large membranous wing similar in appearance to that of a bat and, like that wing, involving the feet muscles in its operation. The bird's wing, on the other hand, has developed highly specialised features : the membrane of skin is replaced by a complex system of feathers, which interlock to form, as we shall see, a very efficient organ for flying. In addition, the bird's wing is harnessed only to the " arm " bones and muscles, and not connected in any way with the legs. This latter is an important modification, since it enables the bird to keep its feet quite free from the flying mechanism and to use them as independent units.

Let us see first how an individual feather is constructed, and from that go on to consider how a bird's wing is built up from such feathers, and how their arrangement leads to the production of an efficient mechanism for flight. Feathers are composed of keratin, which has a chemical composition common to horn, hooves, hair, wool and all similar body growths. That is why, when feathers or wool or horn, are burned, they all smell alike ; the smell of a blacksmith's shop. A single flight feather, Fig. 19 A, consists of a stout main shaft roughly circular in cross section near the root, but flattening and thinning as it approaches the tip. From the central shaft radiate smaller shafts, called " radii " or " barbs " which in their turn support very fine structures



FIG. 18.—*Meadow pipit* (Top) *and yellow wagtail* (Bottom) *removing artificial faeces in experiments made to test the colour awareness of these birds.*

Y→
↑
P
↑
R
Y→
G→
R→
W→

known as " barbules." On one side of the radii, these barbules are composed of flat spines, whilst on the other side, which rests on top of the spines attached to the adjacent radius, the barbules contain a number of hooks known as " barbicels," which engage the upper surface of the spines with a strong interlocking action. In other words we have a series of " hooks " and " eyes " in the fine feather structure which interlocks the whole system and gives the wing cohesion within itself, attended by great flexibility. Fig. 19 D shows a magnified cross-section through adjacent barbs, and illustrates the interlocking action of the hook-bearing barbicels with the adjacent spiny barbules. Figs. 19 A and B are typical flight feathers, which are of two kinds. In any flight feather, the barbs radiating from the central shaft, supporting the intermediate " webs " which make the main body of the feather, are much shorter on one side of the shaft than the other. This side is always that which faces the forward direction of flight, when the wing is spread, or in modern aerodynamic language, the " leading-edge " of the feather is the narrow one. The hinder web of the feather is broader and overlaps the feather next to it. Normally, the narrow forward facing web of a feather has a fairly constant width along its whole length, and this applies also to the wider, rearward facing web too. Such a feather is seen at A in the figure. But sometimes, a few of the long flight feathers which form the tip of the wing have both forward and rear webs which are *not* a constant width along the feather length, but narrow perceptibly in a sudden " step," as shown in B. Such a phenomenon is known as " emargination," and, as we shall see presently, it plays a vital part in giving aerodynamic stability to the wings of many birds.

In Fig. 19 E is shown the upper and under view of the wing of a large bird of prey. The main flight feathers are known as primaries and secondaries (together often loosely called the pinions), while the rest of the wing is composed of smaller softer feathers, called upper and under wing coverts or tertiary wing feathers. When spread, the wing forms a rigid, compact and light structure, shaped convex on top, and capable of amazingly flexible and complicated motions, with changes in shape, size and angle of movement all

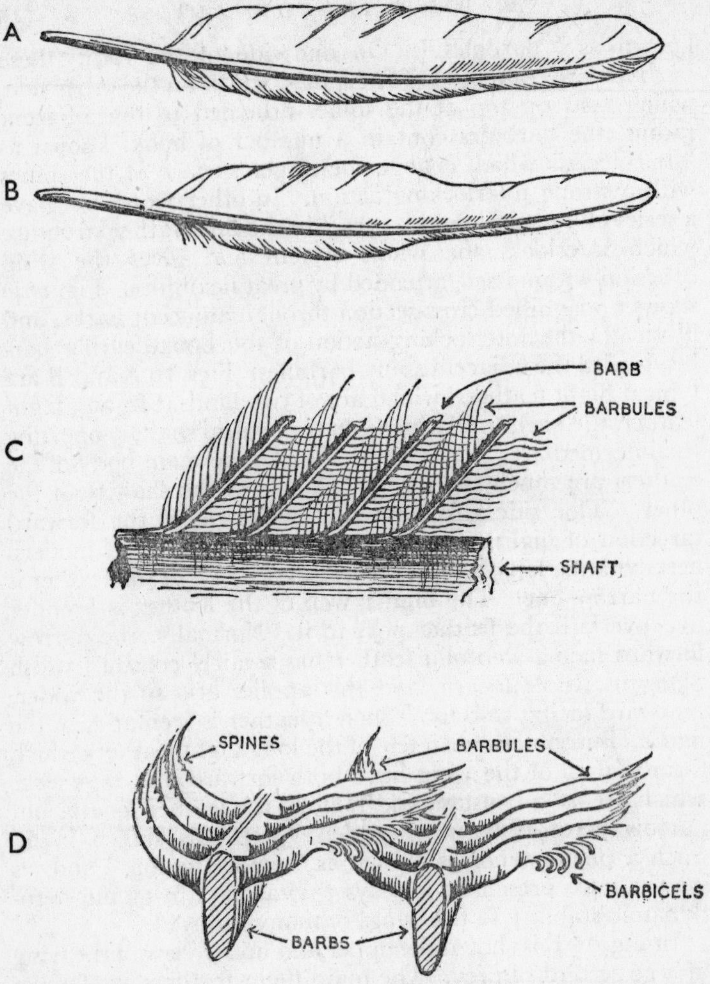

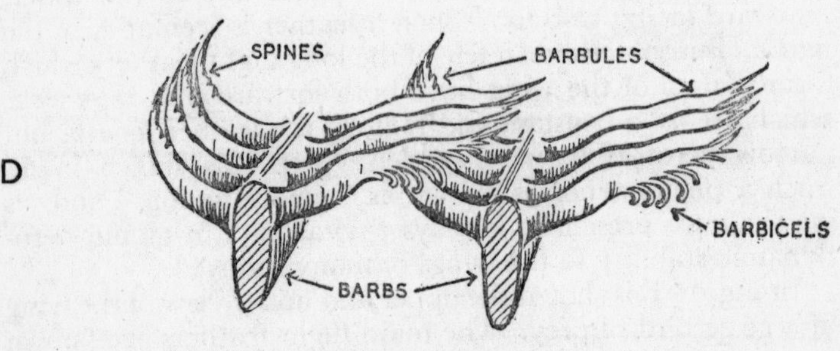


FIG. 19

*A shows a single flight feather.*
*B shows an emarginated flight feather.*
*C Greatly magnified view of part of feather.*
*D Greatly magnified cross-section across two adjacent barbs, showing the way the spines and barbicels interlock.*

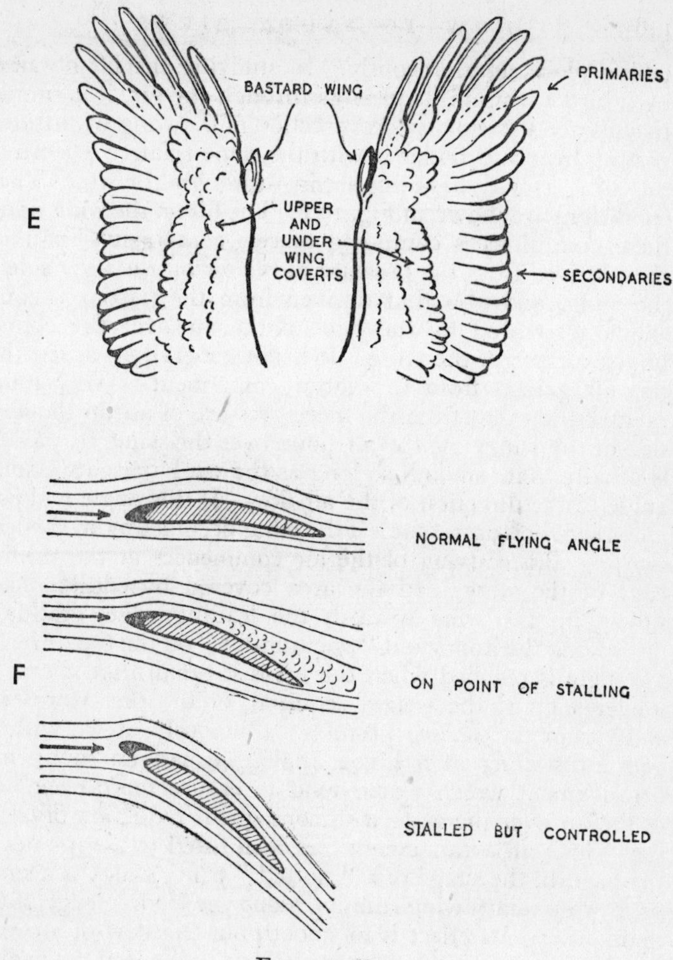


FIG. 19 ii

*E The top pair of figures show (left) the upper, and (right) the under wing of a bird of prey. Note how the emargination of the primary flight feathers gives a series of slots, which are extended by the bastard wing.*

*F The lower figures show how a slotted wing on an aeroplane reduces eddying at the stalling angle. The arrows represent the relative motion of the air-stream.*

taking place simultaneously. In studying the lift obtained by a bird's wing in its passage through the air, it is simpler to consider a stationary cross-section of the wing with the air passing over and under it with the same relative velocity as the wing would have in passing through the air. These conditions are shown in Fig. 19 F. The lift on the wing under these conditions is composed of two components, namely, that derived from the pressure of the air on the *under* side of the wing, and also that derived from the partial vacuum which is created by the flow of the air over the convex upper surface of the wing. It is not generally realised that the lift gained from this latter component is very much greater than that from the mere pressure of air on the *under* side of the wing. As the air flows over the wing, its passage is usually quite smooth so long as the wing presents a small angle to the direction of the air-flow. If this angle is slowly increased, however, that is if the wing becomes more vertical, swirling and eddying of the air commences at the trailing edge of the wing, and the area covered by eddies moves slowly up the wing towards the leading edge, gradually destroying the important " vacuum-lift " on the top. Finally an angle is reached when the lift is so small that it can no longer support the weight required, or in other words the wing is in the *stalling* position. Obviously, if we wish to prevent stalling at a given angle, we can do so by any arrangement which would tend to ensure more even flow of the air over the wing with consequent reduction of eddying. Such an arrangement has been fitted to aeroplanes in the past, in the shape of a " slotted " wing, which is a small narrow auxiliary wing running along the leading edge of the main wing. Its effect is to smooth out the flow of air over the wing and give a much slower stalling speed. Turning now to the bird's wing, we find a very similar arrangement is achieved by making use of the emargination of certain of the flight feathers, and also by the presence of the " bastard wing " (see Fig. 19 E). The bastard wing consists of one main feather, overlaid by one or two smaller ones to give it rigidity. This little group of feathers bears the same relation to the main feathers of the wing as the thumb does to the fingers in the human hand, and is situated about half-way along the leading edge of a wing. When a wing is spread and is approaching what would normally be a stalling angle, the flight feathers of the wing-tips, if they are emarginated, tend to splay out and form a series of regular multiple slots. Their formation is automatic, and is due to the air-pressure forcing them apart. When they have been forced apart a certain distance, the interlocking mechanism of the barbicels, already referred to, comes into play to hold the slotting in position, and we thus have a line of slots covering part of the edge of the wing and extending round the tip. This latter extension, breaking up as it does the round end of the wing-tip into a series of " fingers," also reduces turbulence, since such an arrangement reduces air spill over the *end* of the wings, as well as ensuring more even flow of air over the surface of the wing. The " slot " principle is extended along the leading edge of the wing by the " bastard " wing, acting in the same way as the splayed primaries. Emargination of the primaries is very common in those birds which soar a lot, like eagles, ravens, rooks, choughs and jackdaws, and also in those birds with square or rounded wings like the game birds. It is normal in aeronautics to talk of the " aspect ratio " of a wing. A wing which is long in comparison with its breadth is known as a *high aspect ratio* wing, and conversely, one which is short and broad is a wing with a *low aspect ratio*. In general birds whose wings have a high aspect ratio, like terns, gulls, and most waders have few slots, whilst the birds with low aspect ratio wings, like the pheasant, partridge, vulture, and so on, have many slots which are also deep and long.

As compared with soaring flight, the aerodynamics of flapping flight are complex, for not only is there complex angular movement of the wing through the air, but there is also a different *rate* of movement, at different stages, of the outer and inner sections of the wing. Actually, a bird's wing propels the bird through the air by means of a motion not unlike that used by a boatman when he works a single oar over the stern of a rowing boat. It is essentially " screw-like " in respect of lifting and propulsive power, although acting as a reciprocating propeller and not as a rotating one.

Birds which have a low wing area compared with their

weight (game birds, some song birds, the ducks and so on) beat their wings fast, whilst those with a large area of wing for a given weight (herons, swans, pelicans, the larger gulls) flap their wings slowly. Thus the pelican beats his wings about once per second ; the common house-sparrow about 13 times a second. The need for this is obvious, but is made greater by the fact that the total resultant lift from a given area of wing varies as *the square of the air-speed* ; in other words, if the air speed is doubled, the lift is increased four-fold. Hence heavy birds with small rounded wings can, by flying faster, quickly obtain sufficient lift for their weight.

We can turn now to a consideration of the sensations felt by a bird once it is properly air-borne, and it is here that a great amount of muddled thinking has taken place in the past, leading to a large number of fallacies which have been repeated so often, that it is only with the greatest difficulty that they are being corrected. The fallacies have arisen mainly because of the difficulty most people have of being able to forget that the sensations felt by a person or animal on the ground from the passage of wind *past* them, are totally different from those felt by a living object once it has left the earth's surface and is using the air itself as the supporting medium for passing from one part of the earth's surface to another. The problem is mainly one of relative motion. Consider a man seated in the basket of a balloon firmly held to the ground by ropes. A 10-miles-an-hour wind is blowing, and if the man sits facing this wind, he feels a wind-pressure on his face and body as is produced by such a moving air-current. Now suppose the tethering ropes of the balloon be released. The balloon lifts itself and the man into the air, and *almost immediately* begins to drift along with the wind, assuming exactly its direction and speed relative to the earth. The man now no longer feels any pressure from the wind at all ; he has been transferred from a place where the wind had motion relative to himself, to another where he and the wind have no motion at all relative to one another. Unless the man looks down at the earth, he will imagine that he is suspended quite stationary in a dead calm. If he looks down at the earth, he will realise that he is moving relative to it with a velocity which is exactly equal to that of the air current on which he is floating. This brings us to the enunciation of what may be termed the first law of current-borne objects, namely, that *air- or water-borne bodies rapidly assume the velocity and direction of flow of the current in which they find themselves.* This needs a very slight qualification, for it is obvious that the more ponderable a body (or alternatively the higher its inertia) the more slowly it will assume the velocity of the supporting current. A big, heavily laden ship released in mid-stream from its anchor-hold, will take longer to assume the direction and velocity of flow of the current, than a piece of wood thrown in at the same time and place. To a certain extent the same distinction will hold for large and small birds, but to nothing like the same degree, since even the largest birds have so small an inertia that there must almost immediately be superimposed upon them, the speed and direction of the air current on which they are air-borne.

But a bird's motion in the air is more complex than that of a balloon, or of a floating object in water. A balloon floats in the air because, filled with hydrogen or helium, it is less dense than air ; a piece of wood floats on water for the same reason. A bird, on the other hand, has weight, and is definitely heavier than an equivalent volume of air. It can therefore only support itself in the air by means of a positive motion through the air and relative to it. This it does by propelling itself through the air with its wings. But, one may be asked, how is it then that birds can be seen traversing the air without any perceptible wing-movement ? The answer to this question has been much more clearly understood since the advent of " gliding " by means of sailplanes. We now know that when birds gain great heights by soaring *without attendant wing-movements* they are making use of *ascending* air-currents which are usually associated with certain specific atmospheric conditions, and are normally to be found underneath the large white clouds known as " cumulous " clouds. Beneath these clouds, strongly ascending air currents are often to be found which may have a rate of vertical lift as high as 40 feet per second. There is reason to believe too, that these ascending air currents are rather like huge " bubbles " of air, continually expanding and changing in vertical velocity, so that it is possible to observe a bird in such a current actually being lifted at a higher rate than other birds above or below it, yet soaring in the same current. Those bird-watchers who look at birds in the air and study their ways should note, therefore, the weather conditions under which birds indulge in true soaring flight, that is, in flight which attains height without wing movement. It is probable that such occurrences will be found to be associated with somewhat special atmospheric conditions. One observer in a glider was making use of a particularly strong upward current in South Africa, when, glancing over the side of the cockpit, he saw that he was surrounded by a large number of vultures who were doing just the same as he was, swinging round and round in the uprushing air with wings held rigidly outwards, and taking not the least notice of the glider and its pilot. So it went on until at about 3000 feet, birds and glider reached the undersurface of the large cumulus cloud associated with the upcurrent, and the glider had to descend.

As far as the actual pressure felt by a bird's body in the air is concerned, there can be only one true answer, although in the past this question of imaginary differences of pressure between the air on one side of a bird's body and that on the other, has been invoked in a remarkable manner. It has been used, for example, to explain how birds find their way across the sea on migration, and in an analogous case, in another medium, to explain the remarkable voyage of young eels across the Atlantic in terms of an ability to swim across the North Atlantic drift (" The Gulf Stream ") at a given angle by making use of the " difference in pressure " felt by the two sides of the eel's body in such a procedure ! Actually, of course, no such pressure difference ever exists, and this brings us to a second law which can be applied to the way of a bird in the air, namely, " *a bird maintains itself in the air only by reason of a forward velocity relative to the air, and can feel no pressure from that air other than that caused by this positive relative velocity.*" Since the motion of the bird *relative to the air* must always be a forward one, the force felt by a bird from any wind or air current is always *head on.* This question of relative motion can be quite confusing at times, but it is best to imagine the bird confined in a large cube of air which is being moved over and above the surface of the earth by some unseen hand. An analogous case is that of a fly inside a railway compartment with the windows shut. The speed of the train may be 60 miles an hour relative to the ground, but the fly is conscious only of the fact that if it wishes to transfer itself from one side of the carriage to the other, it can do so by flying at say 10 miles an hour either way, in the perfect calm of the enclosed compartment. Its speed relative to the ground would be 70 miles an hour if it flew in the same direction as the train's motion, and 50 miles an hour if it flew in the opposite direction. But for the fly, the amount of energy expended is identical either way and it is conscious only of a pressure equivalent to a current of 10 miles an hour. The same thing happens with a bird : it is conscious only of the air-pressure due to its own self-made motion relative to the air, and in so far as this is true, a bird can never really be said to struggle against a wind as we struggle, for instance, when bicycling against a head wind. All a bird can know is that it is taking it a longer or shorter time to go from one point on the earth's surface to another according to whether the wind is in the opposite or same direction as the desired motion. It is this "time factor" that is the important consideration with a bird, and which finally exhausts it by compelling it to fly for a period longer than its limit of endurance.

Since a bird is normally conscious only of flying in a complete calm, stories that birds always fly head to wind to prevent their plumage being ruffled from behind are palpably wrong. It is quite another matter that they rest *on the ground* facing the wind, for under such conditions, the wind can, and does, ruffle a bird's feathers unless the bird faces it. The person who can grasp the fundamental difference between these two causes will have no difficulty in appreciating the main facts of a bird's sensations in the air. A slight note of caution is necessary, however, about the question of a complete calm existing round a bird in the air. Near the earth's surface, a certain amount of eddying of the air takes place due to buildings, hills, valleys and contours generally. Such gusts of wind are often sudden and violent and it is sometimes true that birds near the earth's surface do, for a fraction of a second, get struck by a gust with a consequent lifting of feathers. But the inertia of a bird is so low that it almost instantly assumes the velocity of the gust and is once more in a dead calm. This momentary feather lifting may often be seen when a bird like a sparrow or a starling comes suddenly round the corner of a large building where the air-currents are most complex. But these considerations are mainly special cases, and it is true that at a relatively low altitude above the earth's surface, the currents of air are surprisingly free from eddying, or any appreciable gusts. This is apparent from a study of the shapes of clouds at any one height. Although they are of the lightest vapour and would immediately respond to any pressure variations upon them, cloud formations in any one stratum of the atmosphere are usually remarkably constant in shape, pointing to a perfectly calm environment.

We are now in a position to consider the movements of a bird which is flying from one place A on the earth's surface, to another place B. We can once again use the analogy of a boat in a stream, the points A and B being on exactly opposite sides of the bank, the line joining them being at right angles to the current. We suppose that first of all we put an experienced boatman in the boat at A and tell him to navigate the boat to B. What does he do? Being an old hand, he does not head continuously for B, but he heads for a point upstream from B and at such a distance from it that the current is nicely allowed for, and, whilst his boat is always *pointing* at this same angle to A B, its actual passage across the stream is a straight line from A to B. This course may be correctly calculated by making use of a mathematical dodge known as the "triangle of velocities." Thus in Fig. 20 (left) we have the case of a boat crossing a stream from A to B, with a current flowing equal to $V_1$. To get the course necessary so that the boat, whose velocity can be considered as $V_2$ (where $V_2$ must be greater than $V_1$) may cross exactly from A to B, we mark off from A, a distance AX to represent $V_1$, the velocity of the current, and then with a pair of compasses, describe an arc of length to represent the speed $V_2$ of the boat. Where this arc cuts AB, at

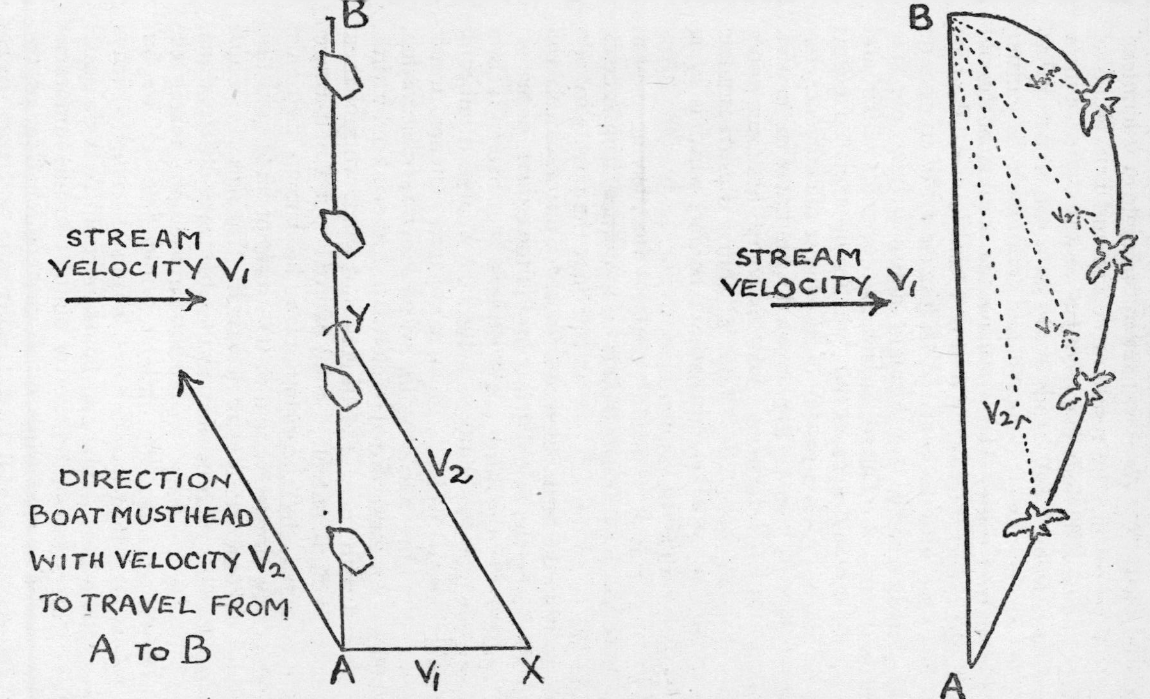


FIG. 20.—*Showing the difference between a calculated course, (left) and a " duffer's " course, (right).*

Y we join with X. We now have a "triangle of velocities," and AY represents the resultant course and velocity. But this lies along AB which is the course we want. Hence if the boat starts from A and heads across on a course parallel to XY, it will actually go along AB, and accomplish the journey in the shortest route. Here we have the method of the old hand, the expert. But put an ordinary land-lubber, afloat for the first time, into the boat and let him steer. What does he do? He heads his boat straight across stream, pointing always towards B. The stream sweeps him along with it, and *his* course is a long curve, as shown in Fig. 20 (*right*). He ends up by reaching B but rowing dead against the current. His is the "duffer's" course as compared with that of the expert, but he will scarcely realise that his course has been other than straight across. The "duffer's" course is also that taken by a fighter plane which, in chasing a bomber which is flying a straight course, heads continuously for the bomber. Airmen know it as a "pursuit" course. Transferring now to the bird passing through the air on a journey from A to B, what are we to think? Are we to admit the possibility of a mind within the bird which consciously or unconsciously will direct it along the calculated course of the expert, or are we to assume for the bird the "duffer's" course? It is a question which can only be solved by a large number of observations, in which a great many bird watchers would need to combine in a co-ordinated piece of mass observation. When we look for recorded results of the routes taken by birds, combined with speed and direction of wind, we find them practically non-existent. So we can only get a half-answer to our query, by theorising from the known degree of intelligently directed action in the world of birds, and this, it must be confessed, is extremely small. The lack of directive action in birds leads us then, in the absence of observational data to the contrary, to plump for the bird taking the "duffer's" course, but there is a big field for *practical* inquiry here. Bird-watching is a practical science which is essentially a field hobby and far more could be done out of doors with a stop-watch and a simple aero-dynamometer than weeks of theorising in an armchair. One or two observers have started on the right lines and their results have already helped a great deal though they are admittedly far too scanty as yet. Such watchers have reported that birds often arrive from over-seas on migration *facing* the wind if this was normally across their main direct route, whilst if the wind was parallel to their route (so that it introduced no drift) then they came in with a following wind. This facing of the wind by a bird arriving at its destination is, of course, demanded by the "duffer's" route, because the bird is bound to finish up face to the wind. This *may* be the basis of the idea that migrating birds prefer to fly into a wind. The assumption of the "duffer's" route for birds has been adopted by some authorities because it explains simply how a bird arrives at its destination. One has only to assume that a bird has an inherent ability to sense the direction of a desired place on the earth (regardless of whether it can be seen or not) and also the ability to fly at a speed (relative to the earth) which is greater than the speed of the air current which is supporting it, and then, *provided the bird flies long enough*, it is bound, by continually facing the desired spot, to arrive there sooner or later. It is an attractive theory, which would be strengthened if direct observation could prove that the bird's route is invariably the "duffer's" route. Up to now, we just do not know. Observations on starlings, flying as they do constantly in packs from feeding grounds to roosts in winter, offer splendid possibilities of solving this problem. One observer noticed that starlings on such a route, when there was a strong cross wind, progressed along by alternately rising up into the wind and then letting it sweep them along and down in a curving drop till they nearly reached the ground, and then rising up again and repeating the performance. The birds' route was then a series of curves and it has been suggested these are in reality a series of joined "duffer" routes, the birds flying from one prominent landmark to another, the route from one landmark to the next being, in effect, a single "duffer's" course, after which the birds start again and so on.

The speed with which birds fly is, fortunately, known with much greater accuracy than the routes on which they fly, although it is only since the motor car came, with its speedometer, that we have obtained true results. The early ornithologists thought that 200 miles an hour was a reasonable speed to assume for many birds ; we now know that only on the rarest occasions does any bird approach this velocity. The "stoop" of a peregrine falcon probably approaches this speed, whilst the spine-tailed swift, a bird found in India, has been timed at 200 miles at hour on several occasions, though it is not stated whether there was a following wind or not. One observer, who used a stop-watch for timing birds over a measured distance and a dynamometer for measuring the force and direction of the wind, was able to show that any one species of bird under normal conditions has a fairly constant speed of flight *relative to the wind*, though a wind can of course, turn the speed of the bird's flight *relative to the earth* from a rapid one to a slow one according to its own direction and force. This fairly constant speed is characteristic of any one species, and varies from species to species. By correcting his results for the speed of the wind, this observer showed that herring gulls fly with an almost constant velocity, relative to the wind, of 20 m.p.h., and swallows at 26 m.p.h. The ground speed of birds has been obtained from motor cars by observing birds flying a course parallel to a road and finding the speed of the car which just maintains pace with the flying bird. Under these circumstances another observer obtained the following table of speeds for birds in flight :

| *Species.* | *Ground Speed.* | |
|---|---|---|
| Rook | 24 to 35 | m.p.h. |
| Jackdaw | 19 | " |
| Starling | 25 to 30 | " |
| Greenfinch | 35 to 36 | " |
| Linnet | 26 to 36 | " |
| Yellow Bunting | 26 to 35 | " |
| Yellow Wagtail | 22 to 30 | " |
| Pied Wagtail | 25 | " |
| Blue Tit | 21 | " |
| Blackbird | 29 | " |
| Song-Thrush | 30½ | " |
| Mistle-Thrush | 35 | " |
| Swallow | 23 to 32 | " |

| *Species.* | *Ground Speed.* |
|---|---|
| House-Martin | 24 to 27 m.p.h. |
| Sand-Martin | 31 ,, |
| Cuckoo | 27 ,, |
| Tawny Owl | 21 to 45 ,, |
| Kestrel | 35 to 38 ,, |
| Heron | 24 to 25 ,, |
| Wood-Pigeon | 27 to 51 ,, |
| Stock-Dove | 40 to 59 ,, |
| Turtle-Dove | 42 to 51 ,, |
| Lapwing | 24 to 40 ,, |
| Gulls | 20 to 25 ,, |

Most of these recorded speeds were taken with little or no breeze blowing, and certainly cannot be in error by more than $\pm$ 5 miles per hour. It will be seen that a speed of more than 50 miles an hour without a following wind must be regarded as exceptional, although on one occasion flocks of guillemots, razorbills and puffins slowly overtook and passed a destroyer doing 37 miles an hour *against* a head wind of 10 miles an hour. Their air speed must hence have been nearly 50 miles an hour. There is little doubt, however, that for the ordinary unexceptional business of their daily lives such as flying from one feeding ground to the other and like operations, most birds are content with a speed of round about 25 to 30 miles an hour. Such data as we possess point, however, to the fact that birds may use a higher velocity of flight in migration. Thus the following table summarises what we know of the speed of migration of certain species compared with their ordinary day-to-day speed :

| | Ground Speed (miles per hour) | |
|---|---|---|
| Bird. | Migration. | Ordinary. |
| Rook | 38 to 45 | 29 to 35 |
| Swallow | 34 to 37¾ | 29 to 32 |
| Lapwing | 37 to 45 | 30 to 40 |
| Starling | 43 to 49 | 25 to 30½ |

As far as migration is concerned, there is reason to believe that much of it is performed at fairly high altitudes if the weather is suitable. In fact it has been suggested, probably with considerable justification, that any migration we actually *see* is not normal migration but the movement of birds forced down towards the ground level by adverse conditions higher up. That atmospheric conditions may, when they are favourable, greatly facilitate migratory movement at high altitudes is shown by the following Air-Ministry figures for wind velocities, at different altitudes, on a normal day chosen at random :

| Altitude. | Velocity of Wind. (miles per hour) |
|---|---|
| Ground Level | 11 |
| 300 ft. | 25 |
| 1000 ft. | 30 |
| 10,000 ft. | 65 |
| 30,000 ft. | 100 |

Thus a bird climbing to 1,000 feet, might, if the wind were favourable, add 19 miles an hour to its speed at ground level for the same expenditure of energy. At 10,000 feet, its speed would be increased by 54 miles an hour ! Here again, the altitude at which birds fly on migration has probably been somewhat over-estimated in the past, especially as most early records were judgments of the height of birds passing across the face of the moon. Since the coming of the aeroplane, however, more accurate results have been obtained, and we now know that for the smaller birds, little migration occurs at heights greater than 3,000 feet. Larger birds can, and do, go higher. Lammergeiers, godwits, curlew and choughs, have been seen on Everest above the 20,000 feet mark, whilst the record for the greatest height of any bird was that of a flock of geese accidentally included in a photograph taken in India of an eclipse of the sun. The height was accurately deduced as nearly 29,000 feet. A point to notice about the table given above of the wide variation in the speed of the air currents at different altitudes, is that the directions of these different currents may vary considerably. It would not be safe to assume, for example, that if we saw a lot of woodcock in a November dawn come in off the North Sea, that they had had to face all the way across the south-westerly gale which was blowing at ground level. Higher up they might well have found an air current in a totally opposite direction, and of equal or even greater velocity.

Here then, in the study of the way of a bird in the air, we have a fertile field for investigation. Motor cars, gliders, aeroplanes, have all helped to correct many of the wild guesses of former years, but we still need a great deal more data before any really significant conclusions can be drawn, and this applies especially to the routes of birds across the globe.

## CHAPTER 11

### PROBLEMS OF POPULATION

THAT bird numbers fluctuate will be apparent to all who watch birds from year to year, and the lifetime of any one of us will see one species increase while another declines in certain areas even to the point of extinction. Such fluctuations may be temporary or permanent according to the true cause of the variation. During the present century, the corncrake has decreased to a striking degree over most of England, so that in places where, at the beginning of the century, it was common, it is now extremely rare or even quite absent. Investigations have suggested that this decrease is associated with a change in methods of agriculture. Modern mechanised reapers together with the introduction of quickly maturing grasses, have advanced the average time of the hay-harvest by as much as three weeks, so that the corncrake, which nests in and around fields of mowing grass, has no time to get its brood off before the fields are cut. This is but one example of a serious decrease in the population of a single species of bird in comparatively recent times. The kite, which formerly swarmed over the towns of mediæval England and acted as scavenger in the garbage-filled streets has been reduced by modern sanitation and persecution to an artificially upheld remnant in the Welsh hills. On the other hand we have witnessed some striking increases among certain species. The starling is undoubtedly a much commoner bird than it was two hundred years ago. Gilbert White mentions it but twice in the whole of *Selborne*. The fulmar petrel has spread in an amazing way in recent years. Its old stronghold was the rocky islands of St. Kilda where it was noted as breeding in 1697. In 1878 it first appeared on the island of Foula, off north-west Scotland, and since then has spread practically all round the coast of Great Britain and Ireland and has even reached the Scillies. The redshank has increased greatly during the last thirty years and now nests in many inland localities where previously it was quite unknown. We see then that fluctuations of bird population are going on all the time, and if we are to gain useful knowledge from such changes, it is essential that we should give numerical significance to them. In other words, we must, wherever possible, count heads. Now this is not such an easy matter as a census of human population, for we cannot send round forms and then sit back and await their return, all nicely completed. In addition, birds do not in general appreciate our society, and far from staying put in one place, tend rather to remove themselves to another, or hide away from our sight. So the scales are to a great extent loaded heavily against the would-be counter of birds. Attempts have been made to estimate the total number of birds of all species in Great Britain, such attempts being based on counts in cross-sections of typical pieces of country like arable land, pasture, forest, moorland and so on. The final numbers are bound to be of doubtful significance however, for the factor by which the small counts are multiplied is necessarily enormous. One authority puts the number of birds in Britain during any one May, at about 100 millions ; a second at about 120 millions. But although an accurate count of the numbers of small birds like the sparrow or meadow-pipit is one of extreme difficulty, there are certain species which, by reason of their habits, will allow us to obtain quite a good idea of their numbers. Most such birds are characterised by their own large size and the fact that they build large conspicuous nests in prominent places, like the tops of trees, where they are easily visible ; or they may nest in well-defined colonies in fairly obvious places. Such birds are herons, rooks, gulls, gannets and grebes, and it is obvious that we can obtain accurate figures for their numbers if we are prepared to be sufficiently thorough and painstaking in our counting, for we can count them, or their nests, during the breeding season. This does not, of course, make any allowance for non-breeding birds, but a fair estimate of these can often be made, and in any case the error from their omission is not likely to be large. Organising nation-wide counts of birds on this basis, the British Trust for Ornithology has been able to study the population of the heron, great crested grebe, fulmar petrel, and rook. There are about 8000 herons in England and Wales, and continuous records for this bird since the first complete census in 1928 have enabled an index of the heron population to be compiled which clearly shows the annual fluctuation in numbers. Between 1928 and 1939 the herons of the Thames Basin, for example, showed a variation in numbers which was never more than 8 per cent in any one year compared with the 1928 figure. The world population of the gannet has been determined at about 170,000 breeding birds, of which nearly 110,000 breed in the British Isles. At the moment, a wide survey of the numbers of rooks breeding in this country is being undertaken. The rook is one of those birds whose food habits make it important for us to know its numbers, for while it is neither wholly good nor wholly bad as far as the usefulness of its diet is concerned, there is little doubt that a large increase in the rook population might have serious repercussions on arable farming. It is quite simple for the ordinary bird watcher to organise his own counts for a given area, though he will probably be doing a more useful job of work if he works in conjunction with other ornithologists under the aegis of some society such as the British Trust. But counts at rookeries, gulleries or heronries in a given district, carried out regularly year after year, can supply valuable and interesting information. It appears that the numbers of certain species of birds and animals fluctuate regularly during given intervals of time, so that we have cycles which show both maxima and minima in the numbers to be found in any area over, say, a 10-year period. At present we have not a great deal of data to show how far this theory of cyclic changes in population applies to the birds which breed here, and amateur bird-watchers could very well supply such data from close and continuous study of a fixed area.

There are, of course, certain very rare birds the numbers of which it is possible to determine with considerable accuracy. The St. Kilda wren is a bird which, through long isolation on a group of islands far out in the Atlantic, has developed sub-specific plumage characters which distinguish it from our common wren. Its numbers are known very precisely. In 1931 there were 68 nesting pairs of this small bird on the St. Kilda group, and in 1939, an almost identical number was counted. In America, the very rare ivory-billed woodpecker is reduced to 24 birds ; there are 300 trumpeter swans remaining of which less than 20 are wild ; whooping cranes are down to just under 200 birds, and the Californian condor totals exactly 45 birds.

Those going on sea voyages can carry out useful census work by doing counts of birds seen during the course of the voyage. These are known as " transects " and are carried out by counting the numbers and species of birds visible from the ship during successive days and correlating them with the ship's position in latitude and longitude. One such transect on a voyage from London to South America demonstrated the presence of a vast, almost birdless area between the Azores and Barbados. It is instructive to plot the results on a map but, if this is done, it is important to chose an area-true map, such as Bonne's projection, and not a direction-true map, like Mercator's projection, since the latter gives an entirely false idea of the relative areas of the sea in widely differing latitudes, especially away from the Equator.

The chief factor controlling the numbers of birds is quite obviously the rate at which they die, or alternatively the age to which they live, and so the average expectation of life of different species is of intense interest in relation to population problems. Curiously enough, the estimates of the average age of birds in the wild state have, until recently, been very wide of the mark, mainly because they were usually based on the age to which any particular species would live under aviary conditions. This is, however, the *potential* age of the species, and it differs greatly from the average age of that species under wild conditions. Since the advent of the practice of ringing birds (which is primarily done to study their movements) we have been able to obtain some interesting and illuminating facts about the age of wild birds at death. Naturally some birds die younger than others ; others are lucky and escape death to live longer than the average, so ringing returns can not only give us the average age to which a wild bird lives, but also a fair idea of the upper limit of its expectation of life under natural conditions.

Below are given the comparative figures for the ages of four common British birds :

| Species. | Greatest Age. (Aviary). | Greatest Age. (Wild Conditions.) | Average Age. (Wild Conditions.) |
|---|---|---|---|
| Song-Thrush | 17 years | 9 years | 1½ years |
| Blackbird | 20 " | 10 " | 1¾ " |
| Starling | 15 " | 9 " | 1½ " |
| Robin | 20 " | 11 " | 1-1¼ " |

There is a most striking difference between these figures. They show that not only is it rare for a small bird to live under wild conditions to more than about half the age it might attain under aviary conditions, but that the *average* age of small birds is remarkably low, and rarely exceeds two years. Although these results may seem surprising, it can be shown that, for a bird population which is substantially constant in numbers (as for example the robin), such a high mortality would only demand the production from each pair of about four to six fledglings a year.

There is a tendency for the larger birds to live longer than smaller ones. The American screech owl, for example, which has lived to an age of 13 years under wild conditions, attains an average age of 5 years. The barn-owl, whose greatest recorded age under wild conditions is 10 years 4 months, lives to an average age of 3 years 2 months ; horned owls to an average of 2 years, and golden eagles to an average of 4 years.

# CHAPTER 12

## AIDS TO FIELD WORK

THE BIRD-WATCHER is fortunate in more than one particular. His is an inexpensive hobby, for the apparatus needed is not extensive and once purchased will, with care, last a lifetime. The open air and the birds are free for all, and what are required are mainly a sharp eye, an inquiring mind, a passion for the subject and a dogged perseverance. But a sharp eye can be made even more effective by the use of good binoculars, and money spent on a first-rate pair will be amply repaid. An essential in a binocular for bird-watching is that it shall be light in weight ; it is surprising how quickly the arms tire when one has to stand motionless, with binoculars raised to the eyes whilst a shy bird moves across the view. So let the glasses be of aluminium alloy if possible. Magnification may be anything from 6 times (=x6) to 10 times (=x10). Higher degrees of magnification should be avoided as it is difficult enough to hold low-power glasses sufficiently steady, and with high powers almost impossible to get a steady view without a rest or stand of some kind. Focusing should be by a central screw as this is much more rapid than the method which focuses by varying each eye-piece. For long-range work, as at reservoirs or sheets of water, a good telescope of magnification x25 is a great help, but is cumbersome to carry and requires a tripod for effective use.

But the real test of a good bird-watcher is his ability to take good notes. This is not as easy as it seems, and there are a few golden rules which ought never to be broken. The first is, *write it down on the spot*. Never trust to memory. Memory lets you down, and then imagination fills in the blanks with disastrous results. Secondly, write too much rather than too little, in the field note-book. You can always transcribe and condense into a fair note-book when you get home. Record even apparent trivialities; they may turn out to be essentials when the jig-saw of bird behaviour comes to be fitted together. In identifying a bird seen in the field, never record its identity unless you have taken down on the spot its characteristics *before* consulting a work on ornithology. It is fatal to jot down a few notes in the field, go home, look at a coloured plate or detailed description of your bird, and then proceed to write a description of what you have seen. Field notes should record such points as distance away from the bird, direction of light, nature of ground, types of other birds associating with your bird, whether it was at rest or in flight, character of the flight if seen, size and shape compared with other birds known to you, points of structure like size, colour and shape of bill, length and colour of feet and legs, shape of wing, and length of tail. Any distinctive white or coloured marking with their *exact* position should be recorded. Write down any cry or note the bird utters. And finally, although you may be "rotten at drawing," try to make a rough sketch of the bird and fill in details. For close observation of birds at the nest a hide-tent is essential, and doubly so if photography is to be undertaken. From a hide tent the bird-watcher can see many intimate details of bird behaviour which are lost to the more distant viewer. Photography can be an aid to bird-watching but only so long as the obtaining of a photograph is kept rigidly secondary to the observing and recording of bird behaviour. If a camera is carried and used merely to illustrate aspects of bird behaviour, it can be a useful tool in the bird watcher's kit. A small reflex, or a miniature camera is best, especially the latter, as a great many photographs can be taken with a miniature in a very short time. The results may not be up to "exhibition" standard, but stuck into a notebook will be very valuable additions to the notes.

And finally, preserve a scientific passion for the truth, the whole truth and nothing but the truth. Avoid competitive discussions with fellow bird-watchers on lists of rarities seen : they become similar to discussions by fishermen on the size of their catch. Find a man whose interest is not merely in discovering eagle owls, or golden orioles, or surf-scoters (often only in a fertile imagination), but one who, like yourself, wishes to study the way birds live and so to understand what manner of creatures they are. Experiences exchanged will then be knowledge gained.

# CHAPTER 13

## THE MIND OF A BIRD

IN STUDYING the lives of birds by methods similar to those discussed in this book, we are continuously confronted by the difficult problem of interpreting the bird behaviour which we observe. In the fields we see birds behaving in a great variety of ways, many of which are conditioned by factors in the external world which we can see and record, just as we do the actions of the birds. Heat and cold, danger, hunger, the presence of other birds, or animals, or types of herbage ; all these are parts of the general environment of birds and both separately and together they will dictate in varying degree the way birds behave. But the general environment of birds is in large measure also the environment of man, for birds are warm blooded animals which breathe air as we do, are affected by heat, cold, thirst, hunger and a host of similar factors, and in some cases, may die from attacks of bacilli and germs which will also kill us. So when we see birds panting on a hot day, as they do when brooding on exposed nests, we are apt to conclude that they are " feeling the heat " just as we do, or we may say that in winter, the bird we pick up barely alive after a prolonged frost is " faint from hunger." Probably in these specific instances we may not be far wrong in our description, but we are really on the edge of a dangerous slope, for we have started to interpret the reactions of birds in terms of our own experiences. Let us move on from the purely physical side of the bird's life to its emotional side, still describing its actions in terms of our own experience. Immediately, we begin to introduce words like love, affection, self-sacrifice, parental duty and so on. We may say that the cock-bird is " *glad* to see the hen return " ; that she shows her *pleasure* by shimmering her wings ; that she may *admire* the cock's fine plumage colours, and that he in return shows her great *affection* and *love*. All these words are used here to denote a state of mind or emotion felt by human beings in similar circumstances, and we can at once be accused and rightly so, of the cardinal sin of "anthropomorphism," a long word which merely means that we have attributed to birds a personality or mind similar to our own. Here then is the great dilemma: how are we to interpret bird behaviour and describe it adequately, if we eliminate completely the tempting method of analogy with our own emotions and also the language we normally use to describe such emotions? The answer is by no means easy. Some would have us confine ourselves strictly to descriptions of what birds do, and leave out the why and wherefore until such time as a massive accumulation of data gives us an angle on the bird's mind from its own behaviour alone. But will this time ever come? And if it does, will it not involve the invention of an entirely new vocabulary with new terms descriptive of bird behaviour? One such word has already been introduced into biological nomenclature. It is "valency" and is said to denote "meaningful significance," that is, if a set of conditions elicit a given response from a bird, that set of conditions is said to have "valency" for that bird. But this word has already been used by chemists for years to denote an entirely different thing, as every modern schoolboy knows, and this attempt merely accentuates the difficulty of the new approach. The modern biologist has, to a certain extent, been forced into a rather extreme position by the great mass of anthropomorphic writing which trammelled the literature of birds, especially that of the more popular kind, down to the period between the two wars. Things then improved considerably, mainly because a number of scientifically trained biologists began to study birds, not only in the museum or laboratory, but also as living animals in the field. They were naturally horrified by the sentimental interpretations which had been put forward for years to explain the bird behaviour they were witnessing, and they consequently discarded and strenuously avoided any interpretation which had the remotest connection with parallel human emotions in similar circumstances. It is possible that the pendulum has swung too far to the other extreme, and I believe that the analogy method is not wholly impossible provided a rigid check is kept on all facts. Bird-watching becomes almost meaningless unless it helps us to an appreciation of the bird's mind. We have seen how the bird's brain is admittedly somewhat rudimentary and undeveloped in those parts which are normally associated with intelligence and that a great deal of bird behaviour has all the appearance of being directed, not by intelligent reasoning, but by a kind of automatic response to visual patterns and cues. But it is possible also to think of many human actions which, by practice, have been so conditioned that they are performed without intelligent direction being apparent at all. We are apt to regard the bird which flies to the spot in mid-air from which its nest has been removed, as singularly lacking in intelligence, yet men occasionally do similar stupid things under somewhat comparable conditions. Thus a platoon of soldiers had been in the habit of marching across a parade ground for many months to a Nissen hut standing by itself on the far side. The hut was on the right-hand side of the road. One day, for some reason, the commanding officer ordered its removal to the opposite side of the road, whilst the men were away. On returning at night, they marched right up to the old spot where the hut had stood and insisted that *their* hut was, or should be, at that precise spot even though it was in full view just across the road ! It was some time before the men could be persuaded to enter the hut in the new position. Is there so great a difference between the two sets of behaviour ? It is not suggested that such behaviour on the part of men is other than abnormal or that it would be frequently repeated, but the fact that it is possible shows that there may be connecting links between the mind of man and that of birds. Many of our actions which bear similarity to those of birds are those we carry out, as we say, " without thinking." If we are thinking of something else while we are doing an action such as driving a car or tending a machine, we may find ourselves doing all manner of queer things such as turning down the wrong street or driving on too far beyond our destination. If we consider afterwards why we do these things, we shall probably find that the wrong road we turned down had surroundings not unlike those of the correct road, or that rows of similarly shaped houses occurred near the destination we missed. In other words our actions have been conditioned by our external environment, without our bringing thought or intelligent reasoning to bear on the situation. Directly we do this, we see how foolish we have been, laugh, excuse ourselves by saying, " I just wasn't thinking what I was doing," and promptly remedy the matter ! May not such actions point the way to an understanding of the mind of a bird ? Man has become increasingly independent of his external surroundings ; he has *thought* his way over many natural obstacles, but to the bird they are still immense dominating forces which demand an immediate response if it is to survive. The degree to which the bird can bring thought and reason to bear on its own problems is, as far as we can judge, very small indeed, and that degree can only be assessed by observations on the bird's behaviour. A man can tell us why he has followed a particular course of action (or at least he should be able to), but this a bird cannot do, and so no direct observations are possible on its mental processes. We shall not go far wrong in interpreting bird behaviour, however, if we allow to the bird the minimum degree of intelligence which will enable us to give a fair and satisfactory explanation of the behaviour we are studying, and remember that, if two explanations of a bird's actions are possible, one invoking a high degree of intelligence and the other a low degree or even none at all, then the simpler one with low intelligence, is almost certain to be the more correct.

# BIBLIOGRAPHY AND REFERENCES

As STATED in the preface, the preceding text does not contain specific references to the many authorities whose work has been consulted, and whose findings are incorporated in the text, but the sources of such work are clearly indicated in the following bibliography and list of references, so that the reader who wishes to consult the original papers may do so. If a particular statement has no corresponding reference associated with it, it is based on the unpublished work of the writer.

The following books have been widely consulted :


" The Handbook of British Birds." *Witherby et al., London, 1938.*

" Bird Flocks and the Breeding Cycle." *Fraser-Darling, Cambridge, 1938.*

" Bird Behaviour." *T. B. Kirkman, Nelson & Son, 1937.*

" Bird Migration." *A. Landsborough Thomson, Witherby, London, 1942.*

" The Riddle of Migration." *W. Rowan, Baltimore, 1931.*

" The Life of the Robin." *D. Lack, Witherby, London, 1943.*

" Territory in Bird Life." *Eliot Howard, London, 1920.*

" An Introduction to the Study of Bird Behaviour." *Eliot Howard, Cambridge, 1929.*

" The Vertebrate Eye." *Gordon F. Walls, New York, 1942.*

" Bird Watching." *E. Selous, London, 1901.*

" Realities of Bird Life." *E. Selous, London, 1927.*

" Evolution : the Modern Synthesis." *J. Huxley, London, 1942.*


The following are two valuable papers :


" The Companion in the Bird's World." *K. Lorenz, Auk, 54, p. 245-73, 1937.*

" Studies in the Life History of the Song Sparrow." *M. M. Nice, Trans. Linn. Soc., New York, 4 : pp. 1-247.*

# REFERENCES

## Chapter i

*Page in Text*

12 Definition of migration, etc. (*Thomson, "Bird Migration," London, 1942*).

13 Effect of light and activity on incidence of migration. (*Rowan, Proc. Boston Nat. Hist. Soc. 39, 151-208, 1929*).

14 Starlings in London. (*Rowan, "Effect of Traffic and Night Illumination on London Starling," Nature, 139, 668, 1937*).

14 Repeat and Extension of Rowan's Work. (*Bisonnette, J. Exptal. Zool., 58, 1931*).

14 Modification of Rowan's conclusions on Canadian Juncos. (*Woolfson, "Bird Migration and gonad development." Condor 42, p. 93, 1940*).

16-18 Rate of spread of spring migrants over Europe. (*H. N. Southern, British Birds, Vol. 32, p. 4; Vol. 32, p. 202; Vol. 33, p. 34; Vol. 34, p. 74; Vol. 35, p. 114*).

18 Ruby-throated humming bird migration over America. (*Cooke, Bird Migration U.S. Dept. of Agriculture, Bulletin 185, 1915*).

20-21 Discussion on the Homing Pigeon. (*Rivière, British Birds, Vol. 17, p. 123*).

21 Homing of noddy and sooty terns. (*Watson and Lashley, Washington, 1915*).

21-22 Homing experiments with puffins, storm-petrels and Manx shearwaters. (*Lack and Lockley, British Birds, 31, pp. 242-336*).

22 Homing experiments with birds in Germany. (*Rüppell, Vogelzug, 5, p. 53, and J. für Ornith, 84, p. 180*).

22 Lack of homing instinct in Goshawk. (*Rüppell, J. für. Ornith 85, p. 120*).

22 Lack of homing instinct in sharp-shinned hawk.

Page in Text

(*Michener, News from Bird-Banders 13, p. 7, 1938*).

22 Experiments with golden-crowned sparrows. (*Sumner, Condor, 40, p. 127, 1938*).

22-24 Polish Experiment with Storks. (*K. Wodzicki, Nature 141, p. 351, 1938; and 143, p. 857, 1939*).

26 Bird migration over the Sahara desert. (*J. Bowers; Field, p. 116, 1944, and ibid, p. 189, 1944*).

## CHAPTER 2

28, 31 Exponents of the territory theory. (*Altum, " Der Vogel und sein Leben," 1868, Eliot Howard, " Territory in Bird Life," 1920*).

28, 32 Territory theory reviewed. (*D. & L. Lack, British Birds, 27, p. 179, 1933*).

31, 32 Territory in gull colonies. (*Kirkman, " Bird Behaviour," Nelson & Son, 1937*).

32 Social life of Jackdaws. (*Lorentz. Proc. XIII Int. Ornith. Congress, p. 207, 1934 and Journ. für Ornith, 79, p. 67, 1931*).

33, 34 Similarity of threat and nuptial displays. (*Kingston, " Meaning of Animal Colour and Adornment," London, 1933; Julian Huxley, Proc. XIII. Int. Ornith. Congress, 1934*).

35 Aggressive display studied by means of mirrors. (*Brown, British Birds, 31, p. 137, 1937*).

35 Aggressive display of robin. (*Lack, Proc. Zool. Soc., London, 109A, p. 169, 1939*).

36, 37 Useful elementary account of ductless gland system, etc. (*Walker, " The Physiology of Sex," Penguin Books, London, 1938*).

38 Male behaviour of female starling in autumn. (*Bullough and Carrick, Nature, 145, p. 629, 1940; and Bullough, Phil. Trans. Royal Society, B., 1942*).

38 Effect of injecting male sex-hormone into female

Page in Text

canary. (*Leonard, Proc. Soc. Exp. Biol. and Med.* *41, p. 299, 1939*).

38 Drumming of great spotted woodpecker. (*Pullen, British Birds, 37, p. 175, 1944*).

39 Drumming of the common snipe. (*Carr-Lewty, British Birds, 36, p. 230, 1943*).

39-41 Statistical investigation of bird song. (*Cox, British Birds, 38, p. 3, 1944*).

42 Song output of lark and willow-warbler. (*Noble Rollin, British Birds, 37, p. 85, 1944*).

44-46 Habitat selection in birds; psychology factor. (*Lack, British Birds, 31, p. 130, 1938*).

46 Habitat distribution of woodland birds. (*Lack and Venables, Journ. of Animal Ecol. 8, p. 391, 1939*).

47-48 Bearded and crested tits and their habitats. (*Smith, Field, October, 1944*).

## Chapter 3

50 Choice of mate in song-sparrow. (*Nice, Trans. Linn. Soc. 4, New York, 1937.*)

51 Recognition of one another among robins. (*Lack, "Life of Robin," Chapter XIII, 1943*).

52 How black grouse recognise one another. (*Fisher, "Watching Birds," p. 148, Penguin, London, 1940*).

52 Herring-gull chicks recognising parents and foreign chicks. (*Goethe, J. für. Ornith. 85, p. 175, 1937*).

52 Black-headed gulls' recognition of one another. (*Kirkman, "Bird Behaviour," London, 1937*).

52 Recognition amongst jackdaws. (*Lorenz. Proc. XIII. Int. Ornith. Congress, 1934*).

52-53 Display in birds with similar plumage in both sexes. (*Huxley, J. Linn. Soc. (Zool.) 35, p. 253, 1923*).

52-53 Shelduck display. (*Wynne-Edwards, Nature, 124, 1929*).

*Page in Text*

54 Mass stimulation in colony-nesters. (*Fraser Darling, "Bird Flocks and Breeding Cycle," Cambridge, 1938*).

55 Display in redshank. (*Smith and G. R. Edwards, The Naturalist, 1935*).

56 Display in great crested grebe. (*Huxley, Proc. Zool. Soc., London, p. 491, 1914*).

57 Pigeons without feathers, displaying areas of bare skin. (*Cole and Owen, J. Heredity, p. 35, 3, 1944*).

57 Display in bullfinch. (*Tucker, British Birds, 32, p. 41, 1938*).

57 Display in barn-owl. (*Smith and Hosking, British Birds, 37, p. 55, 1943*).

58-59 Nest site selection. (*C. & D. Nethersole-Thomson, British Birds, 37, pp. 70, 88, 108, 1943*).

59-61 Nest construction in birds. (*Ryves, British Birds, 37, pp. 182, 207 ; 1943*).

62 Multiple nest-building in blackbird. (*Southern, British Birds, 31, p. 56, 1937*).

63 How the tree creeper builds a nest. (*Ross, British Birds, 37, p. 110, 1943*).

64 Polygamy in corn-bunting. (*Ryves, British Birds, 28, p. 1 ; p. 154, 1934*).

64 Polygamy in the common wren. (*Kjuijver et. al. Limosa, 13, pp. 1-51, 1941*).

65 Polygamy in redshank. (*Williamson, British Birds, 32, p. 120, 1938*).

65 Polygamy in eider duck. (*Gross, Auk. 55, p. 387, 1938*).

## CHAPTER 4

67 Extended egg laying in birds. (*Phillips, Auk, 4, p. 346, 1887*).

67 Experiments on effect of removing or adding eggs. (*Emlen, Condor, 43, p. 209, 1941*).

69 Share of sexes in incubation. (*Ryves, British Birds, 37, p. 10, p. 42, 1943*).

*Page in Text*

69 Brood spots and physiology of incubation. (*Tucker, British Birds, 37, p. 22, 1943*).

71 Incubation in song sparrow. (*Nice, Trans. Linn. Soc. New York, 4, 1937*).

71 Share of sexes in incubation in fulmar. (*Richter. J. für. Ornith. 85, p. 187, 1937*).

71 Share of sexes in incubation in yellow wagtail. (*Smith, British Birds, 33, p. 312, 1938*).

71 Starling brooding man's knuckles. (*R. Kearton, " Wild Nature's Ways," p. 52, London, 1922*).

71 Black-headed gull brooding tin lid. (*Kirkman, Bird Behaviour, 1937*).

72 Temperature under incubtaing birds. (*Kendleigh, British Birds, 28, p. 176, 1932*).

72 Prolonging of incubation period through infertility of eggs. (*Henderson, British Birds, 31, p. 58, 1937*).

73 Cock partridge's behaviour on hatch of young. (*Hosking and Newberry, " Intimate Sketches from Bird Life," London, 1940*).

73, 74 Egg-shell disposal. (*Nethersole-Thomson, British Birds, 35, p. 162, 1940*).

74-75 Effect of cold on young birds. (*Eliot Howard, British Birds, 28, p. 285, 1932*).

79 Nest Sanitation in birds. (*Tucker and Blair, British Birds, 34, pp. 206, 226, 250 ; 1939 ; Smith, British Birds, 36, p. 186, 1942*).

85 Fear reaction in wood duck to hawk ; " injury-feigning." (*Saunders, Auk. 54, p. 202, 1937*).

85-86 Appearance of fear-reaction in young birds. (*Baumgartner, Bird Banding, 9, p. 69, 1938 ; Pickwell and Smith, Condor, 40, p. 193, 1938*).

## Chapter 5

88-89 Imprinting in young birds ; following-reactions, etc. (*Lorenz, Auk, 54, p. 245, 1937*).

89 Behaviour of male bittern in captivity. (*Lorenz, Zool. Anz. Suppl., 12, p. 69, 1937*).

*Page in Text*

90 Learning of essential actions by young birds. (*Lloyd Morgan, "Habit and Instinct," London, 1896*).

90-91 Learning of song by young birds. (*Useful summaries of the literature in :—Lack, "Life of Robin," pp. 33-36, 1942, and Huxley, "Evolution. Modern Synthesis," pp. 305-7, 1942*).

92 Experiments to test intelligence of birds by baiting with food. (*Thorpe, British Birds, 37, p. 29, 1943 ; Bulletin of Animal Behaviour, Vol 1, No. 4, 1939*).

95 Intelligence tests with tits. (*Brooks-King, British Birds, 35, p. 30, 1940*).

## Chapter 6

97 Dispersal of young sandwich terns in autumn. (*Landsborough Thomson, British Birds, 37, p. 62, 1943*).

97, 98 Early packing of certain birds in late summer. (*Meiklejohn, British Birds, 31, p. 85, 1937*).

98 Swifts departing in August. (*Southern, British Birds, 38, p. 157, 1945*).

99 Metereological conditions during autumn migration. (*Richie, Proc. Roy. Soc., Edin., 40, 1940*).

99 Migration of North American golden plover. (*Landsborough Thomson, Bird Migration, London, 1942*).

101-104 The problem of partial migration. (*D. Lack, British Birds, 37, pp. 122, 143, 1943*).

## Chapter 7

107-110 Starling roosts and flight lines. (*Marples, British Birds, 25, p. 314, 1931 ; V. C. Wynne Edwards, British Birds, 23, pp. 138, 170, 1929*).

110 Male behaviour of female starling in autumn. (*Bullough and Carrick, Nature, 145, p. 629, 1940,*

Page in Text

*also Bullough, Phil. Trans. Roy. Soc. 231, B, p. 165, 1942).*

110 Suggested separation of British race of starling as physiological sub-species. (*Bullough, Ibis, Jan., 1945*).

112 Roosting habits of certain species of birds. (*Dunsheath and Doncaster, British Birds, 35, p. 138, 1941*).

113 Gilbert White's reference to flocks of female chaffinches. ("*Selborne,*" *letter 13 to Barrington*).

114 Sex of wintering flocks of ducks. (*Homes, British Birds, 36, p. 42, 1942*).

114-116 20-10 seconds diving rule of Dewar. (*Dewar, British Birds, 33, p. 58, 1939*).

116 Diving tests on duck. (*Ingram, British Birds, 35, p. 22, 1941*).

116-117 The dipper under water. (*Ingram and Dewar, British Birds, 32, pp. 59, 103, 160, 1938*).

117 Pellet ejection in birds. (*Tucker, British Birds, 38, p. 51, 1944*).

117 Food of curlew deduced from pellets. (*Hibbert-Ware and Ruttledge, British Birds, 38, p.* [illegible], *1944*).

## Chapter 8

118-130 Wall's book, "*The Vertebrate Eye*" (*Cranbrooke Institute of Science, New York, 1942*), contains a good bibliography of all the papers consulted in writing Chapter VIII. In addition, the following works are specially recommended: On the structure of birds' eyes. (*Wagner Beitrage Zur Anatomie der Vögel, Akad, Munchen, Bd. 2, p. 271, 1837*).

129 On the structure of the pecten. (*Rabl, Leipzig, Engelmann, 1900; Menner: Die Bedeutung des Pecten im Auge des Vögels. Zool. Jahrbh. Abt. f. allg. Zool und Physiol der Tiere, Bd. 58, p. 481, 1938*).

*Page in Text*

127-129 Visual cells in retinæ of birds' eyes. (*Franz, Vergleichende Anatomie des Wirbeltierauges, Bd. III., p. 989, 1934*).

## Chapter 9

131 Evolution of colour vision. (*Walls, J. Applied Physics. 14, p. 161, 1943*).

132 Colour vision in birds and oil-droplet mosaic first studied. (*Krause, 1863*).

133 Absorption of light by coloured globules in retina of domestic hen. (*Roaf, Proc. Roy. Soc. 105, B., p. 371, 1930*).

134-135 Testing colour vision of domestic fowl and pigeon by illumination of food with spectral colours. (*Hess, Handbuch der vergleichenden Physiol. Bd. 4, pp. 1-200, 1912 ; Watson and Lashley, J. Animal Behaviour, vol. 6, p. 26, 1915-16*).

135 Hue discrimination in pigeon. (*Hamilton and Coleman, Jour. of Comp. Psychol. Vol. 15, pp. 183-191, 1933*).

135-136 Colour vision of Australian grass-parakeet. (*Bailey & Riley, Trans. Roy. Canad. Inst. Vol. 18, p. 47, 1931 ; Plath, Zeits. für vergl. Physiol, Bd. 22, pp. 691-708, 1935*).

136 Colour response in birds, tested by effect on pupil of eye of different colours. (*Abelsdorf, Arch. für Augenheilk, Bd. 58, pp. 64-66, 1907 ; Laurens, J. of Physiol. 64, pp. 97-119, 1923 ; Erhardt Zool. Jahrbk. Bd. 41, pp. 489-502, 1924*).

137 Red-coloured flowers attracting humming birds. (*Porsch, Biologia Generalis, Bd. 7, p. 647, 1931*).

137, 138 Study of Australian Satin bower-bird. (*Nubling, Australian Zoologist, 1941*).

139-141 Colour awareness in the yellow wagtail and meadow-pipit. (*Smith, Nature, p. 376, 1942*).

142 Colours in the feathers of birds. (*Bancroft, J. Phys. Chem., Jany., 1942 ; Frank, J. für Ornith., 1939*).

*Page in Text*

142-143 Red pigment in feathers of touracons. (*Rimington, Proc. Roy. Soc. B., 1938*).

## Chapter 10

145-149 Study of birds' wings with relation to formation of "slots" and safety devices. (*Graham, British Birds, 24, p. 2 et seq., 1930*).

149 Soaring and flapping flight discussed. (*Horton-Smith, "Flight of Birds," Witherby, London, 1929*).

151, 152 Laws governing air-borne bodies. (*Ackworth, "The Cuckoo and other Bird Mysteries," London, 1944*).

154 Calculated and "duffer's" courses discussed. (*C. V. Alexander, Field, Feb. and July, 1944*).

157 Course of starlings flying in strong cross wind. (*Day, Field, Mar., 1944*).

157 Courses of migrating birds at Dungeness. (*Joy, Field, Dec., 1943*).

157-159 Speed at which birds fly. (*Harrison, British Birds, 28, p. 86, 1934; B. B. Roberts, British Birds, 25, p. 220, 1931*).

160 Velocity of wind at different altitudes. (*Horsley, Field, Oct., 1944*).

160 Altitude at which birds fly, especially on migration. (*Harrison, Review of published data, Nature, 127, 1931*).

## Chapter 11

162 Investigation into decrease in the numbers of the corn-crake. (*Norris, British Birds, 38, p. 142, 1945*).

162 Fulmar petrel enquiry. (*Fisher and Waterston, J. Animal Ecol. 10, pp. 204-72, 1941*).

162 Redshank enquiry. (*Thomas, British Birds, 36, p. 5, 1942*).

*Page in Text*

163 Estimates of total number of birds in Britain in May. (*Nicholson, Daily Mail, Sept. 29, 1932 ; Fisher, " Birds as Animals," London, 1939*).

163 Census of great crested grebe. (*Harrison, British Birds, 26, pp. 62, 102, 142, 174, 280, 1932*).

164 Census of herons, and heron " index number." (*Nicholson, British Birds, 22, pp. 270, 334, 1929 ; 23, p. 324, 1930 ; and Alexander, British Birds, yearly reports on heron between 1931 and 1945*).

164 Gannet census. (*Fisher, British Birds, 32, p. 162, 1932 ; Fisher and Vevers, J. Animal Ecol. 12, pp. 173-213, 1938 ; and J. Animal Ecol. 13, pp. 49-62, 1944*).

164 Count of St. Kilda wren, with data on other very rare birds. (*Harrison, Discovery, Sept., 1944*).

165 Counting numbers of birds on sea voyage ; a " transect." (*Nicholson, British Birds, 24, p. 266, 1930 ; Venables, British Birds, 33, p. 152, 1939*)

165-166 Age to which birds live. (*Lack, British Birds, 36, pp. 166, 197, 1942 ; Sumner, Condor, 42, p. 39, 1940*).

## Chapter 12

167-168 How to record sight records of birds. (*Witherby, British Birds, 23, p. 343, 1930*).

168 Field identification of birds. (*Alexander, British Birds, 38, p. 89, 1944*).

168 The camera and the bird. (*Hosking and Newberry, " The Art of Bird Photography," London, 1942*).

## Chapter 13

169-172 Valuable discussions on the mind of a bird are to be found in the works, already cited, of Eliot Howard, Kirkman, Lack and Lloyd Morgan.

# BIRDS ON THE BRITISH LIST MENTIONED IN THE TEXT

The Raven. *Corvus corax corax.*
The Rook. *Corvus frugilegus frugilegus.*
The Jackdaw. *Colœus monedula spermologus.*
The Magpie. *Pica pica pica.*
The Slender-billed Nutcracker. *Nucifraga caryocatactes macrorhynchus.*
The British Jay. *Garrulus glandarius rufitergum.*
The Chough. *Pyrrhocorax pyrrhocorax pyrrhocorax.*
The Starling. *Sturnus vulgaris vulgaris.*
The Golden Oriole. *Oriolus oriolus oriolus.*
The Greenfinch. *Chloris chloris chloris.*
The Siskin. *Carduelis spinus.*
The Linnet. *Carduelis cannabina cannabina.*
The British Bullfinch. *Pyrrhula pyrrhula nesa.*
The Common Crossbill. *Loxia curvirostra curvirostra.*
The Chaffinch. *Fringilla cœlebs cœlebs.*
The Brambling. *Fringilla montifringilla.*
The Tree-Sparrow. *Passer montanus montanus.*
The Yellow Bunting. *Emberiza citrinella citrinella.*
The Reed-Bunting. *Emberiza schœniclus schœniclus.*
The Sky-Lark. *Alauda arvensis arvensis.*
The Tree-Pipit. *Anthus trivialis trivialis.*
The Meadow-Pipit. *Anthus pratensis.*
The Rock-Pipit. *Anthus spinoletta petrosus.*
The Yellow Wagtail. *Motacilla flava flavissima.*
The Pied Wagtail. *Motacilla alba yarrellii.*
The White Wagtail. *Motacilla alba alba.*
The British Tree-Creeper. *Certhia familiaris britannica.*
The British Great Titmouse. *Parus major newtoni.*
The British Blue Titmouse. *Parus cœruleus obscurus.*
The British Coal Titmouse. *Parus ater britannicus.*
The Scottish Crested Titmouse. *Parus cristatus scoticus.*
The British Willow Titmouse. *Parus atricapillus kleinschmidti.*
The British Golden Crested Wren. *Regulus regulus anglorum.*
The Bearded Titmouse. *Panurus biarmicus biarmicus.*
The Red-backed Shrike. *Lanius collurio collurio.*
The Waxwing. *Bombycilla garrulus.*

The Pied Flycatcher. *Muscicapa hypoleuca hypoleuca.*
The Chiffchaff. *Phylloscopus collybita collybita.*
The Willow-Warbler. *Phylloscopus trochilus trochilus.*
The Wood-Warbler. *Phylloscopus sibilatrix sibilatrix.*
The Grasshopper-Warbler. *Locustella nævia nævia.*
The Sedge-Warbler. *Acrocephalus schœnobænus.*
The Blackcap. *Sylvia atricapilla atricapilla.*
The Whitethroat. *Sylvia communis communis.*
The Lesser Whitethroat. *Sylvia curruca curruca.*
The Fieldfare. *Turdus pilaris.*
The Mistle-Thrush. *Turdus viscivorus viscivorus.*
The British Song-Thrush. *Turdus ericetorum ericetorum.*
The Redwing. *Turdus musicus musicus.*
The Ring-Ouzel. *Turdus torquatus torquatus.*
The Blackbird. *Turdus merula merula.*
The Whinchat. *Saxicola rubetra rubetra.*
The Redstart. *Phœnicurus phœnicurus phœnicurus.*
The Nightingale. *Luscinia megarhyncha megarhyncha.*
The Continental Robin. *Erithacus rubecula rubecula.*
The British Robin. *Erithacus rubecula melophilus.*
The British Hedge-Sparrow. *Prunella modularis occidentalis.*
The Wren. *Troglodytes troglodytes troglodytes.*
The St. Kilda Wren. *Troglodytes troglodytes hirtensis.*
The British Dipper. *Cinclus cinclus gularis.*
The Swallow. *Hirundo rustica rustica.*
The Martin. *Delichon urbica urbica.*
The Sand-Martin. *Riparia riparia riparia.*
The Swift. *Apus apus apus.*
The Kingfisher. *Alcedo atthis ispida.*
The Wryneck. *Jynx torquilla torquilla.*
The Cuckoo. *Cuculus canorus canorus.*
The Eagle-Owl. *Bubo bubo bubo.*
The White-Breasted Barn-Owl. *Tyto alba alba.*
The Peregrine Falcon. *Falco peregrinus peregrinus.*
The Kestrel. *Falco tinnunculus tinninculus.*
The Golden Eagle. *Aquila chrysaëtus chrysaëtus.*
Montagu's Harrier. *Circus pygargus.*
The Goshawk. *Accipiter gentilis gentilis.*
The Sparrow-Hawk. *Accipiter nisus nisus.*
The White Stork. *Ciconia ciconia ciconia.*

The Common Heron. *Ardea cinerea cinerea.*
The Grey Lag-Goose. *Anser anser.*
The Mallard. *Anas platyrhyncha platyrhyncha.*
The Teal. *Anas crecca crecca.*
The Common Pochard. *Nyroca ferina ferina.*
The Tufted Duck. *Nyroca fuligula.*
The Scaup Duck. *Nyroca marila marila.*
The Goldeneye. *Bucephala clangula clangula.*
The Common Eider. *Somateria mollissima mollissima.*
The Surf-Scoter. *Oidemia perspicillata.*
The Goosander. *Mergus merganser merganser.*
The Smew. *Mergus albellus.*
The Gannet. *Sula bassana.*
The Storm-Petrel. *Hydrobates pelagicus.*
The Manx Shearwater. *Puffinus puffinus puffinus.*
The Fulmar Petrel. *Fulmaris glacialis glacialis.*
The Great Crested Grebe. *Podiceps cristatus cristatus.*
The Little Grebe. *Podiceps ruficollis ruficollis.*
The Wood-Pigeon. *Columba palumbus palumbus.*
The Stock-Dove. *Columba œnas.*
The Turtle-Dove. *Steptopelia turtur turtur.*
The Oyster-Catcher. *Hæmatopus ostralegus occidentalis.*
The Dotterel. *Charadrius morinellus.*
The Ringed Plover. *Charadrius hiaticula hiaticula.*
The American Golden Plover. *Charadrius dominicus dominicus.*
The Lapwing. *Vanellus vanellus.*
The Turnstone. *Arenaria interpres interpres.*
The Ruff. *Philomachus pugnax.*
The Sanderling. *Crocethia alba.*
The Knot. *Calidris canutus canutus.*
The Curlew-Sandpiper. *Calidris testacea.*
The Common Redshank. *Tringa totanus totanus.*
The Greenshank. *Tringa nebularia.*
The Red-necked Phalarope. *Phalaropus lobatus.*
The Bar-tailed Godwit. *Limosa lapponica lapponica.*
The Black-tailed Godwit. *Limosa limosa limosa.*
The Common Curlew. *Numenius arquata arquata.*
The Whimbrel. *Numenius phæopus phæopus.*
The Common Snipe. *Capella gallinago gallinago.*
The Sandwich Tern. *Sterna sandvicensis sandvicensis.*

The Black-headed Gull. *Larus ridibundus ridibundus.*
The Herring Gull. *Larus argentatus argentatus.*
The British Lesser Black-backed Gull. *Larus fuscus graellsii.*
The Kittiwake Gull. *Rissa tridactyla tridactyla.*
The Razorbill. *Alca torda.*
The Southern Guillemot. *Uria aalge albionis.*
The Southern Puffin. *Fratercula arctica grabæ.*
The Corncrake. *Crex crex.*
The Coot. *Fulica atra atra.*
The British Black Grouse. *Lyrurus tetrix britannicus.*
The British Red Grouse. *Lagopus scoticus scoticus.*
The Common Partridge. *Perdix perdix perdix.*

# FOREIGN BIRDS MENTIONED IN TEXT

Ruby-throated humming bird. *Archilochus colubrus.*
Noddy tern. *Anous stolidus.*
Sooty tern. *Sterna fuscatas.*
Golden-crowned sparrow. *Zonotrichia coronata.*
Song sparrow. *Melospiza melodia melodia.*
Sharp-shinned hawk. *Accipiter velox.*
Red-shouldered hawk. *Buteo lineatus lineatus.*
Wood duck. *Aix sponsa.*
Screech owl. *Otus asio asio.*
Horned owl. *Bubo virginians virginians.*
Blue jay. *Cyanocitta cristata cristata.*
Ivory-billed woodpecker. *Campephilus principalis.*
Trumpeter swan. *Olor buccinator.*
Whooping crane. *Grus americana.*
Californian condor. *Gymnogyps californianus.*
Lammergeier. *Gypaetus barbatus.*
Spine-tailed swift. *Hirundapus caudacutus.*
Canadian juncos. *Junco hyemalis.*
African touracons. *Family : Musophagidae.*
Australian Zebra grass parakeet. *Melopsittacus undulatus.*
Satin bower-bird. *Ptilonorhynchus violaceus.*
Spotted bower-bird. *Chlamydera maculata.*
Newton's bower-bird. *Prionodura newtoniana.*

# INDEX
## (Subject)

# INDEX

## (Authors)

*(Figures in parenthesis refer to page of text ; others, to references)*